Daily TEKS Review

WORKBOOK

Scott Foresman · Addison Wesley

enVisionMATH 2.0

PEARSON

Glenview, Illinois • Boston, Massachusetts • Chandler, Arizona • Upper Saddle River, New Jersey

PEARSON

ISBN-13: 978-0-328-78229-1
ISBN-10: 0-328-78229-7

12   18

Contents

1. Celia used an addition expression to find 6 × 5. Which expression did she use?

   A 5 + 5 + 5

   B 5 + 5 + 5 + 5

   C 5 + 5 + 5 + 5 + 5 + 5

   D 5 + 5 + 5 + 5 + 5 + 5 + 5

2. What is another way of naming 900?

   A 9 ones

   B 9 tens

   C 9 hundreds

   D 9 thousands

3. Los Angeles is one of the largest cities in the United States. The population of Houston is less than that of Los Angeles. Chicago has a population greater than Houston but less than Los Angeles. Phoenix has fewer people than Houston. Which lists the population of the cities from greatest to least?

   A Chicago, Los Angeles, Houston, Phoenix

   B Los Angeles, Houston, Phoenix, Chicago

   C Los Angeles, Chicago, Houston, Phoenix

   D Los Angeles, Phoenix, Chicago, Houston

4. The Perez family is driving to visit relatives. The trip is 184 miles, and they have driven 48 miles. How many more miles do they need to travel?

   _____

5. Order the numbers from least to greatest.

   852   528   582

   _____

6. Compare. Use <, >, or =.

   329 _____ 785

7. **Mental Math** Una put the same number of carnations into 4 vases. If she used a total of 32 carnations, how many are in each vase?

   _____

   _____

   _____

8. Look for a pattern and write the missing numbers.

   2, 8, 14, 20, 26, _____, _____, _____

1. Which of the following shows 564 in word form?

   A Five hundred sixty-six

   B Five hundred sixty-four

   C Five hundred forty-six

   D Five hundred sixty

2. Which numbers continue the pattern?

3, 7, 3, 8, 3, 7, 3, 8, 3, 7, 3, 8

   A 3, 8, 3, 7

   B 7, 3, 8, 3

   C 3, 7, 3, 8

   D 8, 3, 7, 3

3. Which town has the greatest population?

Town	Population
A	1,642
B	1,620
C	1,675
D	1,622

   A Town A

   B Town B

   C Town C

   D Town D

Use the table for **4** and **5**.

Number of Shirts	Number of Buttons
2	8
3	12
6	24

4. The table shows the number of buttons that need to be sewn on different numbers of shirts.

How many buttons are needed for 9 shirts?

_____

5. Mental Math Two workers are each going to sew buttons on 10 shirts. How many buttons will they need in total?

_____

6. Write the number 45,001 in expanded form.

_____

Name _____

1. Which place has the least value in the number 2,387?

    A Thousands place

    B Hundreds place

    C Tens place

    D Ones place

2. How is 3,072 written in expanded form?

    A $300 + 70 + 2$

    B $3,000 + 70 + 2$

    C $3,000 + 700 + 2$

    D $3,000 + 700 + 20$

3. Which shows the numbers in order from greatest to least?

    A 14   41   18

    B 41   14   18

    C 41   18   14

    D 14   48   41

4. Which shows the standard form of the number shown by the model?

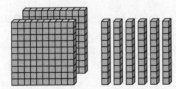

    A 2,069

    B 369

    C 269

    D 69

5. The table shows the number of cars sold each month.

Month	Cars Sold
April	589
May	523
June	651

How many more cars were sold in June than April?

_____

6. Stephanie had 22 marbles. She gave Maggie and Sam each 4 marbles. Explain how you can find how many marbles Stephanie has left.

_____

_____

_____

_____

_____

_____

Name _____

1. Which is twenty thousand, eight hundred twelve written in standard form?

   A 28,012

   B 20,812

   C 2,812

   D 2,012

2. Which symbol would make the equation true?

   36 ◯ 6 = 6

   A +

   B −

   C ×

   D ÷

3. Pat drove 2,648 miles on a trip across the country. What is the distance rounded to the hundreds place?

   A 3,000 miles

   B 2,650 miles

   C 2,640 miles

   D 2,600 miles

4. What is the perimeter of a square that is 3 inches on one side?

   A 15 inches

   B 12 inches

   C 9 inches

   D 3 inches

5. Order the numbers from least to greatest.

   146,552

   145,525

   145,552

_____

_____

6. How would you write the standard form of the number shown by the model below?

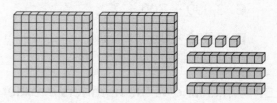

_____

7. Yul tossed a coin 10 times and recorded the results in the tally chart below.

Heads	///
Tails	ℋℋ //

How many more times did the coin come up tails than heads?

_____

8. Compare. Use <, >, or =.

   442,287 ◯ 442,628

1. Which of the following has a 9 in the hundreds place?

   A 199

   B 259

   C 392

   D 923

2. Yvette's computer has a folder with files shown in rows and columns. There are 4 rows and 8 columns. Which number sentence shows how many files the folder has?

   A $4 \times 8 = 32$

   B $8 - 4 = 4$

   C $4 + 8 = 12$

   D $8 \div 2 = 4$

3. Nick has 700 baseball cards. He gives 374 to his younger sister. How many baseball cards does Nick have now?

   A 226 baseball cards

   B 276 baseball cards

   C 326 baseball cards

   D 436 baseball cards

4. What kind of figure has 3 sides?

   A Square

   B Triangle

   C Pentagon

   D Trapezoid

5. What is 549,423 rounded to the nearest thousand?

_____

6. Nina has 465 pennies in a jar. Daryl has 348 pennies in a jar. How many pennies do they have in all?

_____

7. The table shows how many marbles four friends have in their collections.

Marble Collections	
Person	**Number**
Sven	580
Rita	572
Wendy	610
Carlos	602

Write the amounts in order from greatest to least.

_____

1. In the picture below, each square of the grid represents 1 square foot.

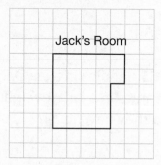

Jack's Room

What is the area of Jack's room?

A 10 square feet

B 17 square feet

C 22 square feet

D 25 square feet

2. Estimation Last year, 288 people saw the school play. This year, 965 people saw the play. Which is the best estimate of how many more people saw the play this year?

A About 300 more people

B About 600 more people

C About 700 more people

D About 1,000 more people

3. Which digit is in the ten millions place of the number 676,590,341?

A 4

B 6

C 7

D 9

4. Which place value would you use to decide whether 4,532 is less than or greater than 4,541?

_____

5. The table below shows the number of flowers a nursery sold during four days.

Day	Flowers Sold
Thursday	59
Friday	132
Saturday	168
Sunday	79

How many flowers in all did the nursery sell during the four days?

_____

Name _____

1. Which digit is in the hundreds place in the number 34,863?

   A 8

   B 6

   C 4

   D 3

2. What are the values of the 5s in the numeral 655,912?

   A 50 and 500

   B 500 and 5,000

   C 5,000 and 50,000

   D 50,000 and 500,000

3. The perimeter of a rectangle is 54 feet. If the length of the rectangle is 12 feet, what is the width of the rectangle?

   Hint: Draw a picture to help you decide.

   A 12 feet

   B 15 feet

   C 18 feet

   D 30 feet

4. The table below shows the cost of each T-shirt depending on how many T-shirts you buy at a store called T-shirts To Go.

Cost of T-shirts				
Number bought	1–5	6–10	11–15	16–20
Cost per T-shirt	$18	$15	?	$9

   Use reasoning and look for a pattern to find the cost per T-shirt if you buy 14 T-shirts.

   _____

5. What are some characteristics of a good math explanation?

   _____

   _____

   _____

   _____

6. Write 8,829,000 in expanded form.

   _____

   _____

1. Marcus has 299 soccer cards. Theo has 436 basketball cards. How many sports cards do these two friends have?

   A 735 sports cards

   B 625 sports cards

   C 263 sports cards

   D 137 sports cards

2. Leroy gave his 63 toy race cars to 9 friends. How many cars did each friend get if they each received the same number of cars?

   A 6 cars

   B 7 cars

   C 8 cars

   D 9 cars

3. Which is the best estimate for the shaded part of the figure shown below?

   A $\frac{1}{8}$

   B $\frac{1}{4}$

   C $\frac{1}{3}$

   D $\frac{1}{2}$

4. Twelve running teams are competing in a cross-country race. The race is 3 miles long. Each team has 5 runners. How many runners are in the race?

   _____

5. Robert owes 5 of his friends a total of $25. He owes each friend the same amount of money. How much does he owe each of his friends?

   _____

6. The Ramblers scored 45 points in the first half of the game and 65 points in the second half. The Staleys scored 36 points in the first half of the game and 76 points in the second half. Which team won the game? Show your computations.

   _____

   _____

   _____

   _____

1. A park baseball league had 54 people sign up to play. Each team will have 9 players. Which number sentence is in the same fact family as $54 \div 9 = \square$?

   A $4 \times 9 = \square$

   B $45 \div \square = 9$

   C $\square \times 6 = 54$

   D $54 \times 9 = \square$

2. The two pie pans below show what was left of two pies.

   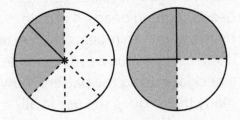

   Which of the following compares the portions of pie left in each pan?

   A $\frac{3}{8} > \frac{3}{4}$

   B $\frac{3}{8} < \frac{3}{4}$

   C $\frac{3}{4} < \frac{3}{8}$

   D $\frac{3}{4} = \frac{3}{8}$

3. In which number sentence does 7 make the equation true?

   A $\square \div 5 = 2$

   B $36 \div 6 = \square$

   C $56 \div \square = 8$

   D $\square \div 4 = 3$

4. On the last day of school, Samantha's class blew up 112 balloons. Thirty-six balloons popped in just a few seconds. How many balloons were left?

   _____

5. Ryan has four pets named Brandy, Bailey, Jimmy, and Sparky. One is a cat, one is a fish, one is a bird, and one is a dog. Brandy is a dog. Bailey is not a bird. Sparky is a fish. What kind of animal is Jimmy? Write the answer in a complete sentence.

   _____

6. A small watch company sells about 35 watches each day. About how many watches does the company sell in one week if it is open every day?

   _____

1. Darlene measures the mass of a small rock in science class and finds it is 6.15 grams. How would she say this number in word form?

   A Six hundred and fifteen hundredths

   B Six and fifteen tenths

   C Six and five tenths

   D Six and fifteen hundredths

2. Terrell bought 12 apples at the fruit stand. He gave some to his friends and had 7 left. How many apples did Terrell give away?

   A 19 apples

   B 12 apples

   C 7 apples

   D 5 apples

3. Which decimal does the model represent?

   A 0.18

   B 0.68

   C 0.86

   D 1.68

4. Write a decimal with a 6 in the tenths place.

   _____

5. The Art Museum had 355,288 visitors last year. The Science Museum had 305,965 visitors. Which museum had closer to 350,000 visitors?

   _____

6. Erika strings a necklace with 5 blue beads, 2 green beads, 4 purple beads, and then repeats this pattern. If she uses 10 blue beads to make a necklace using the pattern, how many beads does she use in all?

   _____

   _____

1. Mr. Thomas divided his class of 35 students into groups to play a game. There were 5 students in each group. Which number sentence is in the same fact family as $35 \div \square = 5$?

   A $5 \times 35 = \square$

   B $\square \times 7 = 35$

   C $70 \div \square = 7$

   D $5 \div 5 = \square$

2. What is the missing number?

   $\$3.87 = 3$ dollars $+ \square$ dimes $+ 7$ pennies

   A 3

   B 7

   C 8

   D 10

3. Carol has 4 bags of oranges. Laverne has twice as many bags as Carol. Which expression represents how many bags Laverne has?

   A 4×2

   B $4 \div 2$

   C $4 + 2$

   D $4 - 2$

4. Monica has tiles that are 1 inch by 1 inch squares. If she uses them to make a rectangle that is 16 inches long and 6 inches wide, how many tiles will she use?

   _____

5. Darryl and 4 friends share 15 apples. How many apples does each friend get if they each receive the same number of apples?

   _____

6. Order 0.21, 0.2, 0.12, 0.02 from least to greatest.

   _____

Name _____

1. Which shows the numbers in order from greatest to least?

   A 3,842, 3,892, 4,201

   B 4,569, 4,274, 3,294

   C 5,301, 5,201, 5,495

   D 6,201, 5,013, 7,329

2. There are 25 students in Mrs. Henley's class. Fourteen of the students are girls. How many of the students are boys?

   A 11 students

   B 12 students

   C 14 students

   D 39 students

3. What is fifty-eight thousand written in standard form?

   A 580,000

   B 58,000

   C 5,800

   D 580

4. Which number has a 6 in the ten thousands place?

   A 652,931

   B 528,629

   C 496,893

   D 360,927

5. Evan has a shell collection. On Monday, he found 6 new shells. On Tuesday, he gave 9 shells to his friends. After giving the shells away, Evan had 37 shells left. How many shells did Evan have to start with?

_____

6. Aretha reads 3 chapters of her book each day. How many days will it take Aretha to finish the book if it has 24 chapters? Write a number sentence to solve the problem.

_____

7. What is 347,492 rounded to the nearest ten thousand?

_____

8. What is the name of the polygon shown below?

_____

Name _____

1. What is seven hundred eighty thousand, two hundred sixteen written in standard form?

   A 780,216

   B 708,216

   C 78,261

   D 78,216

2. Mental Math The fourth-grade class sold 73 tickets for Thursday's basketball game. They sold 99 tickets for Saturday's game. How many tickets did they sell in all?

   A 25 tickets

   B 26 tickets

   C 170 tickets

   D 172 tickets

3. In which place value is the 4?

85.34

   A Hundreds

   B Tenths

   C Hundredths

   D Ones

4. Estimation What is 21,883 rounded to the nearest hundred?

   A 21,900

   B 21,800

   C 21,000

   D 20,000

5. Destiny has 9 more stickers than Shane. Alisa has 7 fewer stickers than Destiny. If Shane has 20 stickers, how many stickers do Destiny and Alisa each have?

_____

_____

6. Jake jumped 3 feet. Marco jumped 5 feet. Peter jumped 4 feet. Together, how much farther did Jake and Peter jump than Marco? Explain how you found your answer.

_____

_____

_____

_____

_____

7. It takes Kiley 5 minutes to run around the track. At that pace, how many minutes will it take her to run around the track 5 times? Write a number sentence to solve.

_____

Name _____

1. **Mental Math** On Friday, Dave read 27 pages of his new book. On Saturday, he read 62 pages. How many pages did Dave read in two days?

   A 99 pages

   B 97 pages

   C 89 pages

   D 79 pages

2. **Estimation** Marco bought a pair of pants for $36 and a hat for $12. About how much did Marco spend?

   A $50

   B $40

   C $30

   D $20

3. A newspaper sold 441,902 copies last week. The editor wants to round that number to the nearest ten thousand for a report. Which number will he use in the report?

   A 400,000

   B 440,000

   C 441,900

   D 442,000

Use the table below for **4** through **7**.

The students at Martha's school were surveyed about their favorite animal they saw at the zoo.

Animals	Votes
Lion	216
Tiger	378
Monkey	192
Bear	139

4. Rounded to the nearest ten, how many students voted for the bear?

   _____

5. About how many students voted for the lion and the tiger all together?

   _____

6. How many more students voted for the monkey than for the bear?

   _____

7. Write a number sentence to show about how many students voted in all.

   _____

Name _____

1. Paula's family sells lemonade at county fairs during the summer. The chart below shows how many cups of lemonade they sold each month.

Lemonade Sales

Month	Number of Cups Sold
May	410
June	1,438
July	4,899
August	2,145
TOTAL	

What was the total number of cups Paula's family sold?

A 8,453 cups

B 8,763 cups

C 8,882 cups

D 8,892 cups

2. Estimation What is 12,389 rounded to the nearest hundred?

A 12,000

B 12,300

C 12,390

D 12,400

3. Estimate the difference by rounding to the nearest thousand.

35,792 − 24,702

A About 12,000

B About 11,000

C About 10,000

D About 9,000

4. Jasmine handed out fliers for a charity event. She started with 75 fliers and ended with 21. How many fliers did Jasmine hand out? Show your work.

_____

5. Mental Math Explain how to use mental math to add 37 + 33.

_____

_____

_____

_____

6. Write the numbers in order from least to greatest.

4.74, 4.72, 4.98

_____

7. Oil is often measured in barrels. One barrel can hold 42 gallons of oil. How many gallons of oil can 7 barrels hold?

_____

1. Which number is thirty-two thousand, four hundred eight written in standard form?

   A 32,480

   B 32,408

   C 30,248

   D 30,240

2. The Wolves sold 4,038 tickets to their soccer game. The Leopards sold 6,224 tickets to their game. How many more tickets did the Leopards sell than the Wolves?

   A 2,186 tickets

   B 2,196 tickets

   C 2,286 tickets

   D 10,262 tickets

3. **Estimation** Alvin rounded the number 336,457 to 340,000. To what place did Alvin round the number?

   A Tens

   B Hundreds

   C Thousands

   D Ten thousands

4. Norman answered the following question below.

   Lilith brought 20 cans to the food drive. Marcus brought 7 cans to the food drive. If Paulina brought 8 more cans than Lilith and Marcus combined, how many cans did Paulina bring?

   Paulina's Donation = ?

20	7	8

   $20 + 7 + 8 = 35$

   So, Paulina brought 35 cans to the food drive.

   Did Norman answer the question correctly? Is his work correct? Explain.

   _____

   _____

   _____

   _____

   _____

   _____

1. Darnell's father is a salesperson who travels all around the state. Darnell made the chart below to show how many miles his father traveled in one week.

Day	Miles Traveled
Monday	234
Wednesday	36
Friday	114
TOTAL	

What total will Darnell write in the chart?

A 384

B 414

C 508

D 708

2. Which numbers are next in the pattern below?

10, 15, 20, _____, _____, _____

A 22, 24, 26

B 25, 30, 35

C 27, 32, 37

D 30, 40, 50

3. A city has a population of about 6,759,000. To which place is the number rounded?

A Tens

B Hundreds

C Thousands

D Ten thousands

4. At the end of last year, Mark's odometer read 74,924 miles. At the end of this year, his odometer read 90,405 miles. How many miles did Mark drive this year?

_____

5. Toby answers 85 out of 100 questions correctly on his science test. Write $\frac{85}{100}$ as a decimal.

_____

6. Allen counted the number of cars parked on 4 streets. On Oak Street, there were 42 cars. On Elm Road, there were 71 cars. On Maple Drive, there were 38 cars. If Allen counted a total of 194 cars, how many cars were parked on Pine Boulevard?

_____

Name _____

1. Express 0.45 as a fraction.

   A $\frac{45}{10}$

   B $\frac{45}{100}$

   C $4 + \frac{5}{10}$

   D 45

2. In one month, a sporting goods store sold 402 pairs of basketball shoes, 137 pairs of running shoes, and 98 pairs of tennis shoes. How many more pairs of basketball shoes were sold than pairs of tennis shoes?

   A 265 pairs

   B 275 pairs

   C 304 pairs

   D 500 pairs

3. A tire company sold 302 tires last week. This week, they sold 488 tires. How many more tires were sold this week than last week?

   A 196 tires

   B 190 tires

   C 186 tires

   D 180 tires

4. Which decimal number is greater, 2.31 or 2.29?

   _____

5. Radha buys a blouse for $8, a pair of jeans for $15, and a skirt for $11. If she pays with $40, how much change will she receive? Show your work.

   _____

   _____

6. Lynne walked 0.75 miles to the post office and 0.6 miles to meet her friend at a park. How far did Lynne walk in all? Use the hundredths grids to help.

   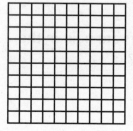 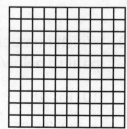

   _____

   _____

1. What is the value of the digit in the hundreds place?

   464,402

   A 40,000

   B 4,000

   C 400

   D 40

2. Tyler has 86 toy cars. Tony has 27 toy cars. How many toy cars are there in all?

   A 113 toy cars

   B 123 toy cars

   C 127 toy cars

   D 131 toy cars

3. The population of a city is 2,592,529. What is the population rounded to the nearest million?

   A 1,000,000

   B 1,500,000

   C 2,000,000

   D 3,000,000

4. In Ms. Sanchez's class, 8 out of the 10 girls are wearing red shirts. What is $\frac{8}{10}$ written as a decimal?

   A 0.08

   B 0.8

   C 8.0

   D 80

5. In a certain election, 5,820,315 people voted for the winning candidate, and 4,295,942 people voted for the losing candidate. Estimate the difference by rounding to the nearest hundred thousand.

   _____

6. Rocky says that he ordered the following decimals from greatest to least. Do you agree? If not, write the decimals in the correct order from greatest to least.

   83.85, 83.86, 83.43

   _____

   _____

   _____

7. Maria bought a shirt for $23.99, pants for $26.99, and shoes for $45.99. How much did Maria pay for all three items?

   _____

8. During the first three games of the season, the attendance for each game was 23,948, 23,853, and 23,973. Which number of people was the greatest?

   _____

Name _____

1. A company is looking to buy property to build a new building. One property is 23.9 acres and the other property is 36.3 acres. How many more acres is the second property than the first property?

   A 13.3 acres

   B 12.4 acres

   C 11.4 acres

   D 10 acres

2. In what place is the digit 7 in the number below?

   83.72

   A Hundreds

   B Tens

   C Ones

   D Tenths

3. Add 36 + 24. Use mental math.

   A 40

   B 50

   C 60

   D 70

4. Which number has a 4 in the millions place, 9 in the thousands place, and 2 in the tens place?

   A 305,480,923

   B 304,869,203

   C 304,694,023

   D 304,689,023

5. Mark has $400 in his savings account. He spends $123 from his savings on a new bike. How much money is left in Mark's account?

   _____

6. Write the numbers in order from least to greatest.

   9,492, 9,174, 9,959

   _____

   _____

   _____

7. Below are Peter's scores for three different rounds of a game. In which round did Peter score the fewest points?

Round 1	Round 2	Round 3
28.03	29.88	28.37

   _____

8. A company shipped 3,492 items this week and 3,630 items last week. How many more items did the company ship last week than this week?

   _____

Name _____

1. **Mental Math** A florist delivered 24 flowers for a birthday party and 48 flowers for a wedding. How many flowers did the florist deliver for both events?

   A 72 flowers

   B 70 flowers

   C 62 flowers

   D 24 flowers

2. Rosita has $10.00. She buys a sundae for $4.00 and a milk shake for $3.00. How much money does she have left?

   A $5.00

   B $4.00

   C $3.00

   D $2.00

3. **Estimation** Bay City has a population of 49,542. What is Bay City's population rounded to the nearest thousand?

   A 49,000

   B 49,542

   C 50,000

   D 60,000

4. Jack bought a sandwich for $4.29, a bag of chips for $0.89, and a drink for $1.39. What was the total cost of all three items?

   _____

5. At its farthest point, the Moon is 252,088 miles away from Earth. Jillene said that the Moon is about 250,000 miles away from Earth. To what place did Jillene round the distance?

   _____

6. Marcy has 1.5 meters of wrapping paper. She uses 0.65 meter of the wrapping paper to wrap a gift for her dad. How many meters of wrapping paper are left? You can use the hundredths grids to help.

   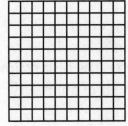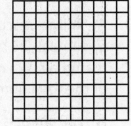

   _____

   _____

1. Jennie has 2 cats, both of which just had kittens. Zippy has twice as many kittens as Fuzzy. Jennie's friends adopt 5 of the kittens. What do you need to know to find out how many of the kittens Jennie keeps?

   A The total number of kittens

   B How old the kittens are now

   C How many friends Jennie has

   D The date when the kittens were born

2. Pedro has saved $72.29. He spends $45.50. How much money does Pedro have left?

   A $26.69

   B $26.79

   C $33.39

   D $67.74

3. An animal rescue center has 51 reptiles, 34 birds, and 16 mammals. Which is the best estimate of the total number of animals?

   A 120 animals

   B 100 animals

   C 70 animals

   D 50 animals

4. A marathon is a running race that is about 26.21 miles long. What is the value of the 1 in this distance?

   _____

5. Write a decimal and fraction for the part of the grid that is shaded.

   _____

6. Write *five and forty-three hundredths* in standard form.

   _____

7. Mount McKinley is located in Alaska. It stands 20,320 feet above sea level. Mount Augusta, also found in Alaska, stands 14,070 feet above sea level. How many feet taller is Mount McKinley than Mount Augusta?

   _____

Name _____

1. **Estimation** Ronni estimated the sum of 149 and 863 by rounding each number to the nearest hundred and then adding. What was Ronni's estimate for 149 + 863?

   A 1,100

   B 1,000

   C 900

   D 700

2. A grocery store had 176 cans of green beans on the shelf on Monday. By Friday, 37 cans had been sold. How many cans were left?

   A 127 cans

   B 139 cans

   C 143 cans

   D 151 cans

3. A page in a photo album holds 6 pictures. A photographer fills 9 pages with pictures. How many pictures were put in the album?

   A 15 pictures

   B 45 pictures

   C 54 pictures

   D 72 pictures

4. Write a number pattern for 8 starfish if each has 5 arms.

5. What number do the place-value blocks below show?

6. **Mental Math** Kyle counted 7 windows on the first floor of a building that has 5 floors. Each floor has the same number of windows. How many windows does the building have?

7. Use the Associative Property of Multiplication to rewrite the expression.

   $(4 \times 5) \times 2$

1. Which digit is in the thousands place in the number 98,732?

    A 3

    B 7

    C 8

    D 9

2. What is the word form of 73,922?

    A Seventy-three thousand, nine hundred twenty-two

    B Seventy thousand, three hundred ninety-two

    C Seventy thousand, nine hundred two

    D Seventy-three thousand, ninety-two

3. Selena rode the train 17 miles last week. Horatio rode the train 24 miles in the same week. How many more miles did Horatio ride the train than Selena?

    A 7 miles

    B 8 miles

    C 31 miles

    D 41 miles

4. Each section of the theater seats 100 people. How many people are in the theater if 7 sections are filled?

_____

5. Anna has 2.64 ft of ribbon and 0.7 ft of yarn. How many feet of ribbon and yarn does Anna have altogether?

_____

6. **Estimation** Shari has $47. How much money does she have, rounded to the nearest ten dollars?

_____

7. Each day, Tom delivers 35 newspapers to each of 8 newsstands around the city. How many newspapers does Tom deliver each day?

_____

1. Sanjay has 6 pages of baseball cards. Each page holds 6 cards. How many cards does he have in all?

    A 12 cards   **C** 36 cards

    B 30 cards   **D** 42 cards

2. **Mental Math** On Field Day, the fourth-grade class splits up into 8 teams of 5 students each. How many students are in the fourth-grade class?

    A 40 students

    B 35 students

    C 25 students

    D 13 students

3. Which grid is $\frac{4}{10}$ shaded?

    A

    B

    C

    D

4. If there are 4 quarters in one dollar, how many quarters are in five dollars?

_____

5. Write 408,032,009 in expanded form.

_____

_____

_____

_____

6. What decimal names the location of point C?

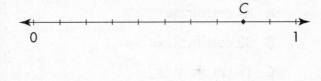

_____

7. Write the number that is ten million more than 842,369,167.

_____

1. The distance between Boston and Cincinnati is 840 miles. The distance between Boston and Philadelphia is 296 miles. How many miles closer to Boston is Philadelphia than Cincinnati is?

   A 644 miles

   B 556 miles

   C 554 miles

   D 544 miles

2. Mr. Kim's class earned 8 perfect attendance certificates in the first quarter. If the class doubled that number in the second quarter, how many certificates did Mr. Kim's class earn in the second quarter?

   A 64 certificates

   B 32 certificates

   C 18 certificates

   D 16 certificates

3. **Mental Math** A scout troop collected 20 pounds of trash on Saturday and twice as much trash on Sunday. How many pounds of trash were collected in all?

   A 80 pounds

   B 60 pounds

   C 40 pounds

   D 20 pounds

4. Show how you can use the Distributive Property to find the product of 7 and 56.

   _____

   _____

   _____

   _____

5. Planks of wood cost $3 each and plywood sheets cost $5 each. Nick purchased 9 planks of wood and 2 sheets of plywood. How much money did Nick spend in all? Show how you solved the problem.

   _____

   _____

   _____

6. List the cities in order from greatest to least population.

City	Population
New Town	2,694,135
Lakeview	2,649,153
Sunny Valley	2,695,314

   _____

   _____

   _____

1. Which digit is in the ten thousands place in the number 630,715?

A 7 **C** 3

B 5 **D** 0

2. The table below shows the number of baseball cards each friend has.

Friend	Number of Baseball Cards
Rita	25
Miguel	50
Len	51
Jodie	60
Angela	250

Which friend has twice as many baseball cards as Rita?

A Jodie

B Miguel

C Len

D Angela

3. Kelly's brother is building towers with blocks. How many blocks will be in the fourth tower?

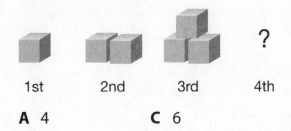

1st   2nd   3rd   4th

A 4 **C** 6

B 5 **D** 7

4. Tommy's allowance is $5.50 per week. How much is that using the least number of dollars and dimes?

_____

_____

5. A store orders 8 boxes of spiral notebooks. There are 144 notebooks in each box. Use breaking apart to show how many notebooks the store ordered.

_____

_____

_____

_____

_____

6. **Mental Math** Mary Ann is saving money to buy a bicycle. If she saves $30 each month, how much money will she save in three months?

_____

1. **Mental Math** A telephone keypad has 3 buttons per row. If there are 4 rows of buttons, how many buttons are on the keypad?

   A 7 buttons

   B 10 buttons

   C 12 buttons

   D 15 buttons

2. Peter jogs 2 miles every day. How many miles does Peter jog in one week?

   A 35 miles

   B 28 miles

   C 14 miles

   D 12 miles

3. Four schools each collect an average of 2,040 pounds of newspapers during a newspaper recycling drive. Use mental math to find how many pounds of newspapers the schools collect altogether.

   A 8,016 pounds

   B 8,106 pounds

   C 8,160 pounds

   D 80,160 pounds

4. Penny wants to buy an electric scooter that costs $180. She also needs to buy a helmet, which costs $38. How much money does she need in all?

   _____

   _____

5. Look at the table below. Write the name of the person who raised the most money and the name of the person who raised the least money. Then explain how you decided.

   Money Raised at Book Fair

Person	Amount Raised
Mr. Grindlow	$287
Ms. Miller	$285
Ms. Daley	$321
Mr. Jameson	$305

   _____

   _____

   _____

   _____

   _____

1. Luis's family is going to the amusement park. Tickets cost $26 for each child. There are 7 children going. How much will all of their tickets cost?

   A $142

   B $162

   C $182

   D $202

2. Traci wants to put the same number of books on each shelf on her bookcase. Which would be the quickest operation to use to figure out how many books go on each shelf?

   A Addition

   B Subtraction

   C Multiplication

   D Division

3. Anthony collects stamps. He started out with 281. His friend Christina gave him 175 more. His sister Kendra gave him 265 more. How many stamps does Anthony have now?

   A 611 stamps

   B 621 stamps

   C 721 stamps

   D 731 stamps

4. Round the number 40,538 to the following places:

   Ten: _____

   Hundred: _____

   Thousand: _____

5. Write the following number in standard form: seven hundred seventy-eight thousand, thirty-nine.

   _____

6. **Mental Math** Warren planted 35 summer squash plants in 7 equal rows of his garden. How many summer squash plants were there in each row?

   _____

7. Jodie drove 4 hours to visit her grandmother. She averaged 60 miles per hour during her trip. How many miles did Jodie travel to see her grandmother?

   _____

Name _____

1. Larry played in 9 basketball games. He scored 10 points in each basketball game. How many total points did Larry score?

   A 19 points

   B 81 points

   C 90 points

   D 100 points

2. Will had 103 trading cards in his collection. He gave some away to a friend. Now Will has 86 trading cards. How many trading cards did he give away?

   A 37 trading cards

   B 27 trading cards

   C 17 trading cards

   D 7 trading cards

3. **Estimation** Ashley read a book that had 183 pages. Then she read another book that had 173 pages. About how many pages did Ashley read in all?

   A 400 pages

   B 300 pages

   C 200 pages

   D 100 pages

4. The product of two numbers is 45. Their sum is 14. What are the two numbers?

   _____

5. Use breaking apart to complete the calculation.

   $4 \times 23 = $ ▇

   _____

6. Cara filled 108 pages in a photo album. If she put 4 pictures on each page, how many pictures are in the album? How do you know your answer is reasonable?

   _____

   _____

   _____

   _____

1. Find 8,365 − 1,174.

   A 6,191

   B 7,181

   C 7,191

   D 7,291

2. **Estimation** A bank bag holds 6,245 pennies. What is 6,245 rounded to the nearest hundred?

   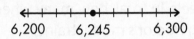

   6,200   6,245   6,300

   A 7,000

   B 6,300

   C 6,250

   D 6,200

3. Which number sentence is true if the number 1,426 replaces the box?

   A 1,326 > ■

   B ■ < 1,467

   C 1,624 < ■

   D ■ = 1,462

4. Which number sentence is NOT in the same fact family as the others?

   A 6 × 9 = 54

   B 9 × 6 = 54

   C 54 ÷ 9 = 6

   D 54 ÷ 3 = 18

5. What number is missing in the equation below? Which property of multiplication is used?

   755 × ■ = 755

   _____

   _____

6. There are 396 adults, 137 children, and 78 dogs living in an apartment building. How many people live in the building?

   _____

7. What are the next two numbers in the pattern below? Describe the pattern, and explain how you used the pattern to find the next two numbers.

   98 87 76 65 54 43 _____ _____

   _____

   _____

   _____

1. Which digit is in the hundreds place in 42,102?

   A 0

   B 1

   C 2

   D 4

2. What time is shown on the clock below?

   A 5:45

   B 5:00

   C 4:45

   D 4:09

3. Mental Math Steve's plant is 12 inches tall. Jennifer's plant is 15 inches tall. How much taller is Jennifer's plant than Steve's?

   A 3 inches

   B 4 inches

   C 15 inches

   D 27 inches

4. Some members of the Ruiz family are getting tickets for Fireworks Night at the ballpark. Tickets cost $5 each. 17 of the tickets they get are for children and 13 are for adults. How much will the tickets cost in all?

_____

5. Hector has 11 model trains. On each model train there are 8 wheels. In total, how many wheels are on Hector's model trains?

_____

6. Estimation Sasha has 8 pets. Lucia has 17 pets. How many pets do they have together, rounded to the nearest ten? Explain how you found your answer.

_____

_____

_____

_____

1. The state fair was open for 4 days. Stewart went to the fair all 4 days. He bought 9 tickets each day. How many tickets did Stewart buy in all?

   A 28 tickets

   B 30 tickets

   C 32 tickets

   D 36 tickets

2. **Estimation** Sid read 6 books on snakes. Each book was 96 pages long. Which shows the most reasonable estimate of how many pages Sid read?

   A $10 \times 100 = 1,000$

   B $10 \times 96 = 960$

   C $6 \times 100 = 600$

   D $5 \times 100 = 500$

3. Carlos is trying out his new scooter. Use the pattern to find how many miles Carlos will ride in 5 hours.

Time (hours)	1	2	3
Distance (miles)	10	20	30

   A 10 miles

   B 40 miles

   C 50 miles

   D 140 miles

4. The chart below shows the number of students enrolled in four elementary schools in the same district. Which school has the most students?

   District Enrollment

School	Number of Students
Adams	4,341
Clark	4,371
Braintree	4,322
Dumont	4,327

   _____

5. The number of fans who went to see the swim meet was 9 times the number of swimmers on the team. If the team has 30 swimmers, how many fans went to see the swim meet?

   _____

6. Write the number 8,011 in expanded form. Explain the value of each digit.

   _____

   _____

   _____

   _____

1. Jan has a beehive that produces 50 pounds of honey each season. How much honey does this beehive produce in 8 seasons?

   A 6 pounds

   B 58 pounds

   C 400 pounds

   D 450 pounds

2. Round 3,689,423 to the nearest hundred thousand.

   A 4,000,000

   B 3,790,000

   C 3,789,000

   D 3,700,000

3. Find 9,050 − 728.

   A 9,779

   B 9,738

   C 9,332

   D 8,322

4. The average person takes in 900 breaths per hour. How many breaths does an average person take in 6 hours?

   A 1,500 breaths

   B 4,500 breaths

   C 5,400 breaths

   D 54,000 breaths

5. Liam earns money by walking his neighbor's dogs. On Monday he earned $20, on Tuesday he earned $15, and on Friday he earned $15. How much did Liam earn this week?

   _____

6. Write the numbers in order from least to greatest.

   0.35, 3.05, 0.03, 3.5

   _____

   _____

7. Danny needs a square saddle blanket for his horse. The length of the saddle blanket is 36 inches. Find the perimeter of the blanket. Show your work.

   _____

   _____

8. Fill in the blanks.

   $5.27 =

   _____ dollars + _____ dimes + _____ pennies

Name _____

1. There are 3,923 students at Westville High School. What is the value of the 9 in 3,923?

   A 9,000

   B 900

   C 90

   D 9

2. Find $600 - 443$.

   A 157

   B 167

   C 257

   D 267

3. Zoe had 10 cookies and made 5 more. Which expression indicates how many cookies Zoe has now?

   A $10 - 5$

   B $10 + 5$

   C 10×5

   D $10 \div 5$

4. Which multiplication fact can help you find $32 \div 4$?

   A 2×8

   B 3×8

   C 4×6

   D 4×8

5. Which symbol makes the statement below true?

   $102,732 \bigcirc 103,832$

6. **Estimation** The folding lawn chairs Mr. Brady likes cost $17 each. He bought 5 of them. Estimate how much money, in dollars, he spent in all.

   _____

7. Find 5×32. Use a drawing to help. Explain the steps you used to find your answer.

   _____

   _____

   _____

Name _____

1. Which does NOT equal 700?

   A 700 × 1

   B 70 × 10

   C 70 × 0

   D 7 × 100

2. **Estimation** Round 325,180 to the nearest ten thousand.

   A 330,000

   B 325,200

   C 325,000

   D 320,000

3. Notebooks cost $4. If Jade buys 3 notebooks, what will be their total cost?

   A $4

   B $7

   C $10

   D $12

4. Which number is greater than 38,246?

   A 37,236

   B 38,236

   C 38,240

   D 38,642

5. Which point on the number line represents 2,475?

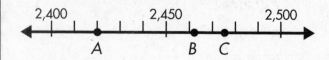

6. **Mental Math** Susan bought 8 packages of colored paper. Each package holds 100 sheets. How many sheets did Susan buy?

   _____

   _____

7. Write three numbers that are greater than 67,000 but less than 68,000.

   _____

   _____

   _____

8. Write the number 302,073 in word form.

   _____

   _____

   _____

D 4·7

Name _____

1. **Estimation** Mrs. Jackson has 806 marigold seeds. How many marigold seeds does she have rounded to the nearest ten?

   A 800

   B 805

   C 810

   D 900

2. Harvey can read 17 pages in one hour. In one week, he spent 6 hours reading. How many pages did Harvey read that week?

   A 102 pages

   B 42 pages

   C 23 pages

   D 11 pages

3. What next three numbers continue the pattern?

   8, 1, 6, 5, 8, 1, 6, 5, 8

   A 1, 6, 5

   B 5, 8, 1

   C 6, 5, 8

   D 8, 1, 6

4. A hardware store has 1,056 boxes of long nails and 502 boxes of short nails. How many more boxes of long nails are there than boxes of short nails?

   _____

5. Wendell has 213 craft sticks. He uses 114 craft sticks to make a model house. How many does he have left over?

   _____

6. There are 24 hours in one day. Write an equation to find how many hours there are in one week. Then explain how you can solve the equation.

   _____

   _____

   _____

   _____

   _____

Name _____

1. **Mental Math** Micah collected shells on the beach during her summer vacation. If she collected 10 shells each day of her 5-day vacation, how many shells did she collect in all?

   A 15 shells

   B 30 shells

   C 50 shells

   D 60 shells

2. Susana has $30. She plans to buy a game that costs $16 and a game that costs $11. How much money will she have left over?

   A $27

   B $26

   C $4

   D $3

3. Mr. Horn, the band teacher, wants to split the band into 4 equal groups. There are 36 members in the band. Which shows how many students will be in each group?

   A 36 + 4

   B 36 − 4

   C 36 ÷ 4

   D 36 × 4

4. Write a multiplication sentence that describes the array shown below.

   _____

5. The distance from Michael's house to his grandmother's house is 84 miles round trip. If Michael visits his grandmother 9 times a year, how many miles does he travel?

   _____

6. Describe how you can find the next two numbers in the pattern.

   8 16 32 _____ _____

   _____

   _____

   _____

   _____

1. Why is 4,532 less than 4,541?

   A It has fewer ones.

   B It has fewer tens.

   C It has fewer hundreds.

   D It has fewer thousands.

2. The table below shows how many magazines four schools sold in a fundraiser. Which school sold the least number of magazines?

School	Magazines Sold
Lane School	1,569
Jefferson School	1,539
Smith School	1,505
Lincoln School	1,560

   A Lane School

   B Jefferson School

   C Smith School

   D Lincoln School

3. **Estimation** Last year, 288 people saw the school play. This year, 91 more people saw the play. What is the best estimate of how many people saw the play this year?

   A 300 people

   B 400 people

   C 500 people

   D 600 people

4. Rick makes 50 picture frames each week. How many frames does he make in 20 weeks?

   _____

5. Kurt has 316 books. Jenna has 321 books. Dale has 99 books. How many books do they have in all?

   _____

6. Mr. Silva has 8 boxes of drills at his store. Each box has 24 drills. How many drills does Mr. Silva have? Explain how you found your answer.

   _____

   _____

   _____

Name _____

1. Nola earns $62 each week walking dogs. About how much money does Nola make in 52 weeks?

   A $3,000

   B $300

   C $110

   D $10

2. Seven students are planning to take an exercise class. If the cost is $12 for each student, how much will it cost for all 7 students to take one class?

   A $80

   B $82

   C $84

   D $86

3. What is 554,303 rounded to the nearest hundred thousand?

   A 500,000

   B 550,000

   C 554,000

   D 600,000

4. Kelly is buying two front row tickets for $35 each and two bleacher tickets for $15 each. How much money will she spend on the tickets?

   _____

5. **Estimation** What is 4,875 rounded to the nearest hundred?

   _____

6. Scott has $49 to spend on model cars. The models cost $9 each. How many models can Scott buy? How much more money will he need to buy another model? Explain your answer.

   _____

   _____

   _____

Name _____

1. A worker makes 49 folding chairs in 1 hour. Which is the best estimate of how many folding chairs the worker makes in 7 hours?

   A 7 folding chairs

   B 50 folding chairs

   C 70 folding chairs

   D 350 folding chairs

2. Madison read 13 pages of her book each day. How many pages did she read in 4 days?

   A 52 pages

   B 42 pages

   C 17 pages

   D 3 pages

3. In which number sentence does 8 make the equation true?

   A $24 \div \square = 3$

   B $36 \div 4 = \square$

   C $63 \div \square = 7$

   D $81 \div 9 = \square$

4. What is the sum of $8{,}237 + 504 + 4{,}730 + 1{,}823$?

   A 14,290

   B 14,294

   C 15,290

   D 15,294

5. **Mental Math** Complete the equations below.

   _____ $\div 7 = 8$

   _____ $\div 8 = 7$

6. Yvette took 21 friends to the school play. Each ticket cost $3. How many dollars did Yvette spend all together on the tickets for her friends?

   _____

7. Max says 14,865 rounds to 14,900. Carl says it rounds to 14,870. Rhoda says it rounds to 15,000. Who is correct? Explain how you know.

   _____

   _____

   _____

Name _____

Carla is keeping track of the number of tomatoes that she picks in her garden. The table below shows the number of tomatoes that she has picked each day this week.

Tomatoes Picked

Day	Number of Tomatoes
Monday	6
Tuesday	4
Wednesday	7
Thursday	9
Friday	6

For **1** and **2**, use the table.

1. What is the total number of tomatoes that Carla has picked so far this week?

   A 30 tomatoes

   B 31 tomatoes

   C 32 tomatoes

   D 33 tomatoes

2. The total number of tomatoes that Carla has picked this summer is 4 times the number she picked on Wednesday and Thursday combined. How many tomatoes has she picked this summer?

   A 64 tomatoes

   B 62 tomatoes

   C 60 tomatoes

   D 16 tomatoes

3. Olivia recorded the following race times during a track meet. Order the times from fastest to slowest.

   23.54   24.92   23.62

   _____

4. Ted has 16 pigs on his farm. He wants to put the same number of pigs in each of 4 pens. How many pigs will he put in each pen?

   _____

5. Jorge went to the store with $200. He bought a sweatshirt for $22 and shoes for $27. How much money did he have left after those purchases? Explain.

   _____

   _____

   _____

1. State parks are popular places to visit. The table below shows how many people visited a park in four different years.

Year	Number of Visitors
2008	40,648
2009	81,355
2010	33,837
2011	54,022

Which choice lists the years in order by greatest to least number of visitors?

A 2008, 2009, 2010, 2011

B 2011, 2008, 2010, 2009

C 2009, 2008, 2011, 2010

D 2009, 2011, 2008, 2010

2. The first Ferris wheel was a hit at the 1893 Chicago World's Fair. Each of its 36 cars carried 40 riders. How many riders filled 20 cars?

A 80 riders

B 600 riders

C 800 riders

D 8,000 riders

3. **Mental Math** Annan ate 1 slice of pizza for dinner. He ate 4 times as many slices the next day for lunch. How many slices of pizza did Annan eat for lunch?

_____

4. At a theme park, 72 people waited to board the SplashMaster water ride. Each car holds 8 riders. How many cars can be filled by the people waiting?

_____

5. Describe the pattern below. Draw the next shape in the pattern.

_____

_____

_____

_____

1. Which table shows the partial products for 26 × 15?

A
	10	5
20	100	200
6	60	100

B
	10	5
20	200	10
6	60	30

C
	10	5
20	200	100
6	600	30

D
	10	5
20	200	100
6	60	30

2. Bill was counting members of his team by fours. The first number he said was 4, then 8, and then 12. What are the next three numbers in the pattern?

A 15 18 21

B 14 16 18

C 16 18 20

D 16 20 24

3. **Estimation** Doug and his mother are driving to visit his uncle. They drive 291 miles each day for 3 days. About how many miles do they drive in all?

_____

4. Lucy's Diner ordered 4 boxes of plastic forks. Each box contained 125 plastic forks. How many plastic forks did Lucy's Diner order?

_____

5. A museum has thousands of shells to see. Tickets cost $7 for adults and $4 for youths. The museum is free for anyone under 5. The Baker family is planning to visit with 7 adults, 6 youths, and 3 children under 5. How much will all of their tickets cost? Explain.

_____

_____

_____

1. What is the number three hundred fifty thousand, nine hundred nine written in standard form?

   A 305,909

   B 305,990

   C 350,909

   D 350,990

2. **Estimation** A basketball arena can hold approximately 7,000 people. Fans bought 5,134 tickets before the game. About how many more seats are left to fill before the game?

   A 5,000 seats

   B 2,000 seats

   C 1,500 seats

   D 1,000 seats

3. **Estimation** Which number is the best estimate for the product of 73 × 47?

   A 2,800

   B 3,200

   C 3,500

   D 4,000

4. Ben is making 17 party favors for his sister's birthday party. Each party favor contains 28 items. How many items will Ben use in all to make the party favors?

   _____

5. **Mental Math** It is approximately 1,000 miles from New York City to Tampa. Suppose a pilot travels one way between New York City and Tampa 6 times in one week. About how many miles did she travel?

   _____

6. The buses for Philips Elementary School carry 40 students per bus. The buses go between 25 and 35 miles in one hour. There are 12 buses that bring students to school each day.

   What piece of information is NOT needed if you want to determine how many students take the bus to school each day?

   _____

   _____

   _____

1. A delivery truck travels 346 miles each day for 5 days. What is the total number of miles the truck travels?

   A 1,500 miles

   B 1,523 miles

   C 1,700 miles

   D 1,730 miles

2. A group of 106 campers sits in a big circle. The camp leader tells the campers to say "hello" to the person sitting next to them on each side. What is the total number of times the campers say "hello"?

   A 226 times

   B 212 times

   C 206 times

   D 202 times

3. If each shaded square is $\frac{1}{10}$, what number does the model show?

   A 0.13

   B 1.3

   C 3.7

   D 13.7

4. One cubic foot of concrete weighs about 145 pounds. What is the weight of 9 cubic feet of concrete?

   _____

5. The graph shows the number of states the students in Mr. Robb's class have visited.

   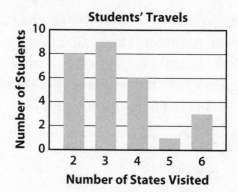

   How many students have visited at least 4 states?

   _____

6. Write this number in word form: 40.32

   _____

   _____

Name _____

1. Which digit is in the ten thousands place in the number 489,725,031?

   A 8

   B 3

   C 2

   D 0

2. There are 27 students in Mrs. Langley's class. Each student does 15 math homework problems each night. How many math problems in all does the class do in one night?

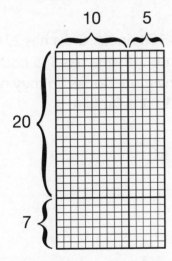

   A 405 math problems

   B 305 math problems

   C 300 math problems

   D 255 math problems

3. José drinks 64 fluid ounces of water each day. How much water does he drink over 35 days?

_____

4. The graph shows the number of cars sold in one week.

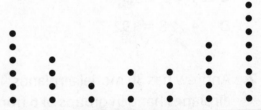

Sun Mon Tues Wed Thurs Fri Sat

Cars Sold

On which day were the most cars sold, and how many cars were sold that day?

_____

_____

5. **Mental Math** Mary Ann is saving to buy an MP3 player for her brother's birthday, which is in December. The MP3 player costs $90. If she starts saving in September, and saves equal amounts each month, how much money will she need to save each of the three months?

_____

1. Elijah has a lawn-mowing business. He has 24 customers and he mows each lawn once a week. Which number sentence shows how many lawns Elijah mows in 8 weeks?

   A $24 \div 8 = 3$

   B $24 - 8 = 16$

   C $24 + 8 = 32$

   D $24 \times 8 = 192$

2. Andrew has 36 model airplanes. The airplanes hang in groups of 6 from his ceiling. Which model shows how many groups of 6 he has?

   A
36	
8	8

   B
36		
12	12	12

   C
36			
9	9	9	9

   D
36					
6	6	6	6	6	6

3. Which list of numbers is in order from greatest to least?

   A 1,223, 1,465, 1,452

   B 17,621, 17,612, 17,654

   C 123,453, 123,457, 123,212

   D 272,738, 272,737, 272,736

4. There are 12 houses in Carlos's neighborhood. Each house has 16 windows. How many windows are there in all?

   _____

5. **Mental Math** Gina bought 8 bags of animal crackers. If each bag holds 9 animal crackers, how many crackers does Gina have in all?

   _____

6. Mark has 188 books, Erika has 274 books, and Christina has 365 books. How many more books do they need to reach 1,000? Explain.

   _____

   _____

   _____

   _____

   _____

1. Grace was born in 1995. How old will she be in 2027?

   A 22 years old

   B 32 years old

   C 42 years old

   D 132 years old

2. The art museum had 72 visitors who signed up for a guided tour. The guide could take 8 people at a time. Which number sentence is in the same fact family as $72 \div 8 = \square$?

   A $8 \times 72 = \square$

   B $\square \times 72 = 8$

   C $8 \times \square = 72$

   D $8 \times 8 = \square$

3. A large marching band has 76 trombones and 110 cornets. How many trombones and cornets are there in all?

   A 186 instruments

   B 184 instruments

   C 86 instruments

   D 34 instruments

4. **Mental Math** Complete the fact family below.

   $6 \times \underline{\hspace{1cm}} = 30$

   $5 \times \underline{\hspace{1cm}} = 30$

   $\underline{\hspace{1cm}} \div 5 = 6$

   $30 \div \underline{\hspace{1cm}} = 5$

5. Marissa has 4 bags of marbles. Each bag has 4 marbles in it. How many marbles does Marissa have in all?

   _____

6. There are 18 people at Nick's birthday party at Pizza Playhouse. Each table can seat 6 people. How many tables do they need?

   _____

7. Write 9,785,420 in expanded form.

   _____

   _____

1. Tisha is organizing her 64 CDs into boxes. Each box holds 8 CDs. How many boxes does Tisha need?

   A 8 boxes

   B 6 boxes

   C 4 boxes

   D 2 boxes

2. **Mental Math** Shannon gave 35 blueberry muffins to 7 friends. How many muffins did each friend get?

   A 4 muffins

   B 5 muffins

   C 6 muffins

   D 7 muffins

3. In which number sentence does 6 make the equation true?

   A $24 \div 8 = \square$

   B $48 \div 8 = \square$

   C $63 \div 9 = \square$

   D $81 \div 9 = \square$

4. Larry reads the same number of pages each night. After 7 nights, he has read a total of 140 pages. How many pages did Larry read each night?

   _____

5. Devin bought 2 packs of yogurt. Each pack had 6 cups of yogurt. How many cups of yogurt did Devin buy?

   _____

6. Complete the fact family below.

   _____ $\div 4 = 5$

   _____ $\div 5 = 4$

   $4 \times$ _____ $=$ _____

   $5 \times$ _____ $=$ _____

7. **Mental Math** Kendra's family plans a trip that is 480 miles long. If they drive the same number of miles each day for 6 days, how many miles will they drive each day?

   _____

1. The Smith family is packing to move. Each moving box holds 30 glasses. There are 3 boxes. How many glasses are there?

   A 90 glasses

   B 60 glasses

   C 33 glasses

   D 9 glasses

2. Samantha drives 2,100 miles each week. How many miles does she drive in 4 weeks?

   A 840 miles

   B 850 miles

   C 8,400 miles

   D 8,500 miles

3. Antonio runs 4 miles each day. How many miles does he run in one year? Remember, one year has 365 days.

   A 2,240 miles

   B 1,640 miles

   C 1,460 miles

   D 1,240 miles

4. Lola is planning a surprise party for her brother. She is inviting 34 people besides her brother and herself. She can seat 6 people at each table. How many tables will Lola need?

   A 5 tables

   B 6 tables

   C 7 tables

   D 8 tables

5. Joe does push-ups, sit-ups, and jumping jacks. He does these in a different order every day. How many different orders are possible? Make an organized list to help you solve the problem.

   _____

6. **Estimation** Estimate the quotient.
   555 ÷ 8

   _____

7. Marissa is planning a community picnic. She has 35 tomatoes that can each produce 7 slices. How many tomato slices will she have?

			.
⓪	⓪	⓪	
①	①	①	
②	②	②	
③	③	③	
④	④	④	
⑤	⑤	⑤	
⑥	⑥	⑥	
⑦	⑦	⑦	
⑧	⑧	⑧	
⑨	⑨	⑨	

1. Isabelle scored 528 points and Brandy scored 285 points in the same game. Which is the best estimate for how many more points Isabelle scored than Brandy?

   A 200 more points

   B 300 more points

   C 700 more points

   D 800 more points

2. Which fraction of the figure below is shaded?

   A $\frac{6}{6}$

   B $\frac{4}{6}$

   C $\frac{3}{6}$

   D $\frac{2}{6}$

3. What is the perimeter of the figure shown below?

   12 in.

   10 in.

   A 22 inches

   B 44 inches

   C 120 inches

   D 240 inches

4. What is the sale price, in dollars, if the normal price is $40?

Sports Store Sales	
Normal Price	**Sale Price**
$15	$12
$21	$18
$27	$24
$40	?

5. Explain how you could use compatible numbers to estimate 245 ÷ 3. Then estimate the quotient.

   _____

   _____

   _____

   _____

1. Quinn read $\frac{1}{4}$ of a book. Jesse read the same amount of the book. Which diagram could show how much of the book Jesse read?

   A

   B

   C

   D

2. Megan has 8 classes each day. How many classes does she have in 9 days?

   A 48 classes

   B 72 classes

   C 86 classes

   D 96 classes

3. Mr. Farina is 42 years old. He is 7 times as old as his daughter. How old is his daughter?

   A 6 years old

   B 7 years old

   C 8 years old

   D 9 years old

4. Ned's grandmother turned 67 in 2012. In what year was Ned's grandmother born?

   _____

5. **Estimation** Doug read 67 pages on Tuesday, 43 pages on Wednesday, and about 50 pages on Thursday. Estimate the total number of pages Doug read over the three days. Explain how you found your estimate.

   _____

   _____

   _____

   _____

6. **Number Sense** Jacklynn received $0.85 in change at lunch on Tuesday. On Friday, she received $0.25 in change at lunch. Without calculating, how can you tell whether Jacklynn received more than or less than $1 in total change?

   _____

   _____

   _____

1. **Mental Math** Alexandra has 24 flowers. She puts the same number of flowers in each of her vases. How many flowers will be in each vase?

A   3 flowers

B   4 flowers

C   8 flowers

D   12 flowers

2. Diana wants to save a total of $1,500 to buy a laptop computer. If she saves $5 per week, in how many weeks will she be able to buy the computer?

A   3 weeks

B   30 weeks

C   300 weeks

D   3,000 weeks

3. Write the numbers 9,856; 9,965; 9,864; and 9,846 in order from least to greatest.

_____

_____

4. Henry wants to buy a pair of speakers that cost $325. So far, he has saved $157. How much more does Henry have to save to buy the speakers?

_____

5. Heather wrote a basic multiplication fact, but she covered up some of the numbers. What multiplication fact did she write? Explain how you found the missing numbers.

☐ × ☐ = 49

_____

_____

_____

Name _____

1. Wayne bought 6 football tickets. Each ticket cost $26. How much money did he spend?

   A $186

   B $182

   C $176

   D $156

2. There are 35 boxes of soup cans on a delivery truck. How many cans of soup are on the delivery truck if there are 30 cans in each box?

   A 1,050 cans

   B 850 cans

   C 625 cans

   D 425 cans

3. Andrea reads 36 pages each night. How many pages does she read in 42 nights?

   A 1,502 pages

   B 1,512 pages

   C 1,552 pages

   D 1,582 pages

4. Daniel recycles 48 aluminum cans each week. How many cans does he recycle in 51 weeks?

   _____

5. **Mental Math** Mugs cost $2 each. How much would it cost to buy 6 mugs?

   _____

6. Richard ran 8 laps around a 400-meter track. How many meters did Richard run in all?

   _____

7. Round 6,852 to the nearest thousand.

   _____

8. Write the number 3,503,672 in word form and in expanded form.

   _____

   _____

   _____

1. Pete is packing toys into boxes. Each box holds 30 toys. There are 94 toys and 3 boxes. How many extra toys are there?

   A 4 toys

   B 3 toys

   C 2 toys

   D 1 toy

2. Samantha drives 95 miles each day. How many miles does she drive in 40 days?

   A 2,800 miles

   B 3,400 miles

   C 3,800 miles

   D 4,800 miles

3. Julie bikes 30 weekends each year. On the weekends when she bikes, she bikes 9 kilometers. How many kilometers does she bike in four years?

   A 270 kilometers

   B 1,000 kilometers

   C 1,080 kilometers

   D 1,180 kilometers

4. Rose is planning a surprise party for her father. She is inviting 94 people besides her father and herself. She can seat 8 people at each table. How many tables will Rose need?

   A 10 tables

   B 11 tables

   C 12 tables

   D 13 tables

5. Joe does 25 sit-ups each day. How many sit-ups does he do in 3 weeks? Remember, one week has 7 days.

   _____

6. **Estimation** Estimate the quotient.
   $522 \div 9$

   _____

7. Jenna needs 3 cups of flour to make 24 of her favorite cookies. How many cups of flour does Jenna need to make 120 of her favorite cookies?

			.
⓪	⓪	⓪	
①	①	①	
②	②	②	
③	③	③	
④	④	④	
⑤	⑤	⑤	
⑥	⑥	⑥	
⑦	⑦	⑦	
⑧	⑧	⑧	
⑨	⑨	⑨	

8. David is making 9 care packages. He divides 45 packs of pumpkin seeds equally among the care packages. How many packs of pumpkin seeds are in each care package?

   _____

   _____

1. Nola earns $62 per week walking dogs. How much money does Nola make in one year? Remember, one year has 52 weeks.

   A $3,442

   B $3,224

   C $3,124

   D $2,134

2. **Mental Math** Seven students are planning to take an exercise class. If the cost is $9 per student, how much will all the students pay for one class?

   A $80

   B $72

   C $63

   D $56

3. Benny has 79 toy cars. He wants to give them to 4 of his friends. He wants each friend to have an equal number of cars. How many toy cars will Benny have left over?

   A 0 toy cars

   B 1 toy car

   C 2 toy cars

   D 3 toy cars

4. Sayid wants to buy 3 sweaters for $37 each and 2 scarves for $11 each. How much will she spend on these pieces of clothing?

   _____

5. Mandi has $52 and would like to buy some magazines. Each magazine costs $8. How many magazines can she buy? How much more money would she need to buy another magazine?

   _____

   _____

   _____

6. Round 9,870 to the nearest hundred.

   _____

7. Sarah has collected 34 sports cards. She shares them equally with her sister. How many sports cards does Sarah give her sister?

   _____

1. Which of the following is **NOT** located between 0.3 and 0.9 on a number line?

   A 0.4

   B 0.5

   C 0.7

   D 5.0

2. Helen and Grace are working on a geography project together. They must find the state capitals for each of the 50 states. They decide that they will each research the same number of states. How many capitals will each girl find?

   A 2 capitals

   B 10 capitals

   C 25 capitals

   D 50 capitals

3. Every year, Kevin's grandmother sends him $20 for his birthday. Kevin always saves his birthday money. He is now 9 years old. How much money has he saved?

   A $200

   B $180

   C $170

   D $100

4. Jorge bought a backpack for $11.99, a notebook for $3.49, and a pack of pencils for $1.35. How much did Jorge spend?

   _____

5. Margo, Linda, and Liz are sisters. Margo is 8. Linda is twice as old as Margo. Liz is 4 years younger than Linda. How much older than Margo is Liz?

   _____

6. Harry drove 687 miles in the past 3 days. If he drove the same number of miles each day, how many miles did Harry drive each day?

   _____

7. What is the value of the digit 6 in the number below?

   158,624,202

   _____

Name _____

1. Hannah has 381 postcards in her collection. She puts an equal number of postcards in each of 6 boxes. How many postcards does she have left over?

   A 5 postcards

   B 3 postcards

   C 2 postcards

   D 1 postcard

2. Mrs. Diaz has 25 students in her class. She assigned each student 34 math problems for homework. How many math problems should her students turn in?

   A 440 math problems

   B 460 math problems

   C 750 math problems

   D 850 math problems

3. Troy's mother works 30 hours per week. How many hours does she work in 50 weeks?

   A 15 hours

   B 150 hours

   C 1,500 hours

   D 15,000 hours

4. Peter reads 208 pages each month. About how many pages does Peter read in a year? Remember, one year has 12 months.

   _____

5. Each bat bag can hold 12 bats. If the team has 3 full bat bags, how many bats are there to choose from?

   _____

   _____

6. A tandem is a bicycle that two people ride at the same time. If 49 people want to ride tandems, how many tandems would be needed? How many people would not be able to ride?

   _____

   _____

   _____

1. **Mental Math** Elizabeth is baking cookies. She has invited 6 people to her house. She wants each guest to have 4 cookies. How many cookies does she need to bake for her guests?

   A 20 cookies

   B 22 cookies

   C 24 cookies

   D 26 cookies

2. **Mental Math** There were 32 students going on a field trip. Each van can carry 8 students. Which number sentence is in the same fact family as $32 \div 8 = \square$?

   A $4 \times \square = 32$

   B $32 \times 8 = \square$

   C $\square \times 4 = 8$

   D $8 \times 8 = \square$

3. **Mental Math** In which of the following does 5 make the number sentence true?

   A $3 \times 2 = \square$

   B $\square \times 6 = 42$

   C $9 \times \square = 45$

   D $\square \times 3 = 18$

4. Jacob's rock collection is shown below. If Dan has 50 times more rocks than Jacob, how many rocks does Dan have?

   _____

5. Arthur, Jorge, and Dylan collected a total of 328 cans to recycle. Arthur collected 105 and Jorge collected 112. How many cans did Dylan collect?

   _____

6. **Explain** Barbara received a music gift card for $35. She used the gift card to download 35 songs for $0.99 each. Can Barbara download another song? How do you know?

   _____

   _____

   _____

   _____

   _____

1. There are 33,201 people living in Harold's town. There are 8,295 people living in Nancy's town. How many people live in both towns?

   A 31,496 people

   B 33,496 people

   C 41,496 people

   D 48,496 people

2. Which of the fractions below is NOT equal to $\frac{1}{2}$?

   A $\frac{2}{4}$ 

   B $\frac{3}{6}$ 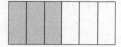

   C $\frac{2}{3}$ 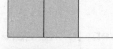

   D $\frac{4}{8}$ 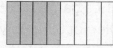

3. Ben's team scored 63 points in the first half of a basketball game. His team won the game by a score of 124 to 103. How many points did his team score in the second half?

   A 21 points

   B 31 points

   C 40 points

   D 61 points

4. A group of 9 students want to share 72 counters equally. How many counters should each student get?

_____

5. Juanita got a score of 23,486 points while playing a video game. The highest score for the game was 25,958. How many more points would Juanita need to tie the highest score?

_____

6. **Estimation** George read 123 pages in a book yesterday and 85 pages today. He plans to read about 200 pages over the next two days. Estimate the total number of pages he will have read over the 4 days. Explain how you found your answer.

_____

_____

_____

Name _____

1. On Monday, a garden center had 402 daisies. By Friday, 103 daisies had been sold. How many daisies were left?

   A 199 daisies

   B 299 daisies

   C 301 daisies

   D 309 daisies

2. Sasha runs 4 miles every day. How many miles does Sasha run in one week?

   A 32 miles

   B 28 miles

   C 20 miles

   D 14 miles

3. Which number sentence is true?

   A $3,592 > 3,585$

   B $7,294 < 4,204$

   C $1,938 = 1,983$

   D $9,302 < 9,299$

4. There are 2,948 students at Central High School. What is the value of the 9 in 2,948?

   A 9

   B 90

   C 900

   D 9,000

5. The distance from John's house to his uncle's house is 75 miles round trip. If John visits his uncle 7 times a year, how many miles does he travel?

   _____

6. **Estimation** What is 6,302 rounded to the nearest thousand?

   _____

7. While on vacation, Mina read 316 pages and Ryan read 179 pages. How many more pages did Mina read than Ryan?

   _____

8. Patrick went to the store with $100. He bought a game for $55 and a controller for $30. How much money did he have left after those purchases? Explain.

   _____

   _____

   _____

   _____

   _____

1. Which digit is in the hundred thousands place in the number 315,674,892?

   A 6   **C** 4

   B 7   **D** 8

2. Jen reads 45 pages each night. How many pages does she read in 30 nights?

   A 135 pages

   B 930 pages

   C 1,150 pages

   D 1,350 pages

3. **Mental Math** There were 48 students going on a field trip. Each van could carry 8 students. Which number sentence is in the same fact family as $48 \div 8 = \square$?

   A $\square \div 8 = 48$

   B $8 \div \square = 48$

   C $48 \times 8 = \square$

   D $8 \times \square = 48$

4. **Estimation** Sophia estimated the sum of 203 and 394 by rounding each number to the nearest hundred and then adding. What was Sophia's estimate for $203 + 394$?

   A 400   **C** 600

   B 500   **D** 700

5. Look at the table below. Write the name of the city with the most people and the name of the city with the least people. Then explain how you decided.

   City Population

City	Population
Groveville	592,059
Highlights City	482,050
Techtown	459,582
Townsville	502,401

   _____

   _____

   _____

   _____

   _____

   _____

   _____

6. Joseph has 56 chickens on his farm. He wants to put the same number of chickens in each of 8 pens. How many chickens will he put in each pen?

   _____

   _____

1. Dylan bought 5 tickets to a football game. Each ticket cost $76. How much money did he spend?

   A $220

   B $270

   C $350

   D $380

2. **Mental Math** In which of the following does 4 make the number sentence true?

   A $3 \times 1 = \square$

   B $\square \times 5 = 20$

   C $7 \times \square = 35$

   D $3 \times \square = 15$

3. Juan's team scored 38 points in the first half of a basketball game. His team won the game by a score of 72 to 63. How many points did his team score in the second half?

   A 25 points   C 38 points

   B 34 points   D 40 points

4. There are 49,459 people who live in Sally's town. There are 32,934 people who live in Peter's town. How many people live in these two towns?

   A 71,383 people

   B 71,483 people

   C 81,393 people

   D 82,393 people

5. Paul owns a dog walking business. On weekends, he walks 5 dogs. Write the number pattern for the number of legs for 1, 2, 3, 4, and 5 dogs.

   _____

6. Lina wants to buy a pair of in-line skates for $79. She also needs to buy a helmet, which costs $28. How much money does she need in all?

   _____

7. Find 4×28. Use a drawing to help. Explain the steps you used to find your answer.

   _____

   _____

   _____

Name _____

1. Zoey has 700 stamps. Seth has 392 stamps. How many more stamps does Zoey have than Seth?

   A 492 stamps

   B 388 stamps

   C 308 stamps

   D 298 stamps

2. **Mental Math** To study for a math exam, Sonia completes 10 practice problems each night. How many problems will she complete in the 7 nights before the exam?

   A 17 problems

   B 50 problems

   C 70 problems

   D 80 problems

3. What is 924,290 rounded to the nearest thousand?

   A 920,000

   B 921,000

   C 924,000

   D 925,000

4. Which statement comparing numbers is true?

   A $892 < 883$

   B $892 > 883$

   C $883 = 892$

   D $883 > 892$

5. The table below shows the number of points each friend has.

Final Score

Friend	Points
Keegan	55
Orlando	45
Felicity	80
Shelby	90
Aiden	100

Which friend has twice as many points as Orlando?

_____

6. **Estimation** Elliot drove 175 miles yesterday and 132 miles today. He plans to drive about 300 miles over the next two days. Estimate the total number of miles he will have driven over the 4 days. Explain how you found your answer.

_____

_____

_____

_____

_____

1. Jason bought a package of 45 baseball cards. He plans to give each of 5 friends the same number of cards. How many cards will each friend receive?

   A 9 cards   **C** 7 cards

   B 8 cards   **D** 6 cards

2. **Mental Math** Zach is 10 years old. Sydney is 5 years older than Zach. Logan is 6 years younger than Sydney. How old is Logan?

   A 9 years old   **C** 16 years old

   B 10 years old   **D** 21 years old

3. Kelsey has 300 photos that she wants to put in a photo album. Each page of the album can hold 5 photos. How many pages will she need?

   A 6 pages   **C** 60 pages

   B 30 pages   **D** 90 pages

4. Which multiplication fact can help you find 30 ÷ 6?

   A 6 × 2 = ?   **C** 6 × 6 = ?

   B 6 × 5 = ?   **D** 5 × 4 = ?

5. A group of 8 students want to share 64 counters equally. How many counters should each student get?

   A 8 counters   **C** 10 counters

   B 9 counters   **D** 11 counters

6. Chloe has a dog walking business. She charges $7 for each dog she walks. On Saturday, Chloe walked 6 dogs. On Sunday, she walked 9 dogs. How much money did Chloe earn in all?

   _____

7. Write the number 302,490 in word form.

   _____

   _____

   _____

8. Bentley has $85 to spend on action figures. Each action figure costs $8. How many action figures can Bentley buy? How much more money will he need to buy another action figure? Explain your answer.

   _____

   _____

   _____

   _____

   _____

   _____

   _____

Name _____

1. Josh is saving to buy a necklace for his mother's birthday, which is in 5 months. The necklace costs $125. If he starts saving in January, and saves an equal amount each month, how much money will he need to save each month?

   A $10   C $25

   B $15   D $30

2. Patricia recycles 25 pounds of newspaper each week. How many pounds of newspaper does she recycle in 52 weeks?

   A 1,000 pounds   C 1,290 pounds

   B 1,100 pounds   D 1,300 pounds

3. There are 84 students in the school band. At a band concert, an equal number of students were seated in 4 different sections. How many students were seated in each section?

   A 3 students   C 14 students

   B 7 students   D 21 students

4. Madison and Jasper combined all their pennies. Madison had 392 pennies, and Jasper had 284 pennies. How many pennies did they have in all?

   A 506 pennies   C 706 pennies

   B 676 pennies   D 776 pennies

5. Which digit is in the thousands place in the number 938,294?

   _____

6. Seven friends are planning to go see a movie. If the cost is $17 for each ticket, how much will it cost for all 7 friends to go?

   _____

7. Sebastian is buying two pavilion tickets for $75 each and two lawn tickets for $27 each. How much will he spend on all four tickets?

   _____

8. **Estimation** Estimate the product 8 × 2,193. Show your work.

   _____

   _____

   _____

Name _____

1. Kevin is putting his baseball cards into an album. He has 450 cards and each page of the album holds 9 cards. How many pages will Kevin need if all 450 baseball cards are going in the album?

   A 50 pages

   B 40 pages

   C 25 pages

   D 5 pages

2. The population of Town A is 15,729. Town B has a population of 21,634. What is the total population of the two towns?

   A 35,372

   B 36,799

   C 37,255

   D 37,363

3. Wendy has 8 kinds of seashells in her collection. She has 122 of each kind of shell. How many seashells does she have in her collection?

   A 976 seashells

   B 866 seashells

   C 122 seashells

   D 8 seashells

4. **Estimation** The population of the city that Andrew lives in is 172,648. About how many people live in Andrew's city rounded to the nearest thousand?

5. Use the figures and the number pattern to write the missing numbers in the table.

Number of Stories	7	6	5	4	3
Number of Blocks	21	18	15		

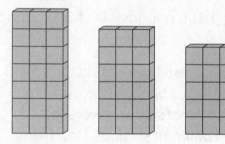

6. A canning company packs 24 cans of peas in each box it ships. How many cans of peas are shipped in 50 boxes?

1. Which shows 200,601 in word form?

   A Two hundred thousand, six hundred one

   B Two hundred six thousand, one

   C Twenty thousand, six hundred one

   D Two thousand, six hundred one

2. Isabel walked 1,357 steps to get to school. Harold walked 935 steps to get to school. How many more steps did Isabel walk?

   A 492 more steps

   B 422 more steps

   C 392 more steps

   D 122 more steps

3. **Mental Math** Carl cut a 30-foot rope into 6-foot sections. How many 6-foot sections will Carl have?

   A 5 sections

   B 4 sections

   C 3 sections

   D 2 sections

4. Pedro has started a car washing business. He charges $5 for each car he washes. On Saturday, Pedro washed 4 cars. On Sunday, he washed 7 cars. How much money did Pedro earn in all?

   _____

5. Anna tutors her friend in math for 30 minutes each day. How many minutes will she tutor in 2 weeks? Remember, there are 7 days in 1 week.

   _____

6. Zak takes 3 steps for every 2 steps Rich takes. How many steps will Zak take if Rich takes 18 steps? Explain how you found the answer. Make a table to help.

   _____

   _____

   _____

   _____

1. Janelle and Howard combined all their pennies. Janelle had 213 pennies, and Howard had 468 pennies. How many pennies did they have in all?

   A 781 pennies

   B 681 pennies

   C 671 pennies

   D 255 pennies

2. Steve picked 72 apples at the orchard. He plans to give all the apples away to 8 friends. How many apples will each friend get?

   A 9 apples

   B 8 apples

   C 7 apples

   D 6 apples

3. **Mental Math** Carla is 8 years old. Leo is 2 years younger than Carla. Katy is 6 years older than Leo. How old is Katy?

   A 4 years old

   B 8 years old

   C 12 years old

   D 16 years old

4. Richard rides his bike 14 miles a day, 7 days a week. Amelia rides her bike 17 miles a day, 6 days a week. Who rides more miles in a week?

   _____

5. **Estimation** Wendy has collected 5,708 shells for her collection. What is 5,708 rounded to the nearest ten?

   _____

6. Marsha's school has 345 students. If all the students are separated into 5 equal groups, how many are in each group?

   _____

7. Jake found that it rained for 14 days out of the last 20 days. What is $\frac{14}{20}$ in simplest form?

   _____

1. Gina buys $\frac{1}{4}$ yard of material to make a pillow. Which fraction is equivalent to $\frac{1}{4}$?

   A $\frac{4}{8}$

   B $\frac{3}{8}$

   C $\frac{2}{8}$

   D $\frac{1}{8}$

2. What fraction of these marbles have stripes?

   A $\frac{1}{4}$ of the marbles

   B $\frac{1}{3}$ of the marbles

   C $\frac{1}{2}$ of the marbles

   D $\frac{3}{4}$ of the marbles

3. Juan has 26 beach balls. Each beach ball has 16 stripes. How many stripes are there in all?

   A 182 stripes

   B 386 stripes

   C 416 stripes

   D 566 stripes

4. Keith has a package of 75 marbles. He wants to share them equally among 8 friends. How many marbles will be left over?

_____

5. Roberto has 5 books. The number of pages in the books are 113, 152, 109, 122, and 131. Order the number of pages from least to greatest.

_____

6. It took Jan 3 hours to do the laundry, walk the dog, and mow the lawn. How many minutes did it take her? Remember, there are 60 minutes in an hour.

_____

7. Write a multiplication fact that will help you find 63 ÷ 7.

_____

1. Which fraction shows the part of the set of circles that are shaded in simplest form?

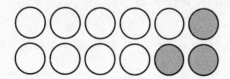

A $\frac{1}{3}$

B $\frac{1}{4}$

C $\frac{1}{10}$

D $\frac{1}{12}$

2. Shawn has a set of 125 marbles. He is organizing his marbles into 5 equal groups. How many marbles should he put in each group?

A 10 marbles

B 15 marbles

C 20 marbles

D 25 marbles

3. **Mental Math** Mary is sharing stickers from her collection with 4 of her friends. How many stickers will each friend receive if Mary shares a total of 36 stickers?

A 40 stickers

B 32 stickers

C 12 stickers

D 9 stickers

4. **Estimation** Estimate the product 9 × 231. Show your work.

_____

_____

_____

5. Write two equivalent fractions for the number of balls that are striped.

_____

6. A tree farm has 209 trees. There are 3 workers to water the all of the trees. If each worker waters the same number of trees, can they complete the job? Explain.

_____

_____

_____

_____

Name _____

1. Which digit is in the thousands place in the number 661,239?

A 9   **C** 3

B 6   **D** 1

2. The two trays of pizza below show the amount of pizza left over after the fourth-grade party.

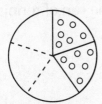 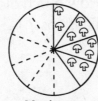

      Mushroom

Which of the following compares the amount of pepperoni pizza left over to the amount of mushroom pizza left over?

A $\frac{2}{5} > \frac{4}{10}$

B $\frac{2}{10} < \frac{4}{5}$

C $\frac{2}{5} = \frac{4}{10}$

D $\frac{4}{10} > \frac{2}{5}$

3. There are 63 students in the school band. At a band concert, Jerome saw that equal numbers of band members were seated in 3 different sections. How many band members were seated in each section?

A 21 band members

B 14 band members

C 7 band members

D 3 band members

4. In January of 2013, Mr. Edwards turned 64 years old. In what year was Mr. Edwards born?

_____

5. What fraction of the triangles are shaded?

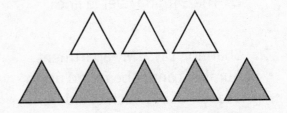

_____

6. Compare using $>$, $<$, or $=$.

$\frac{5}{6} \bigcirc \frac{7}{8}$

7. Estimation What is 1,249 rounded to the nearest hundred?

_____

Name _____

1. Airport security guards choose some travelers for an extra safety check. So far, the guards have chosen the 6th, 12th, 18th, and 24th travelers in line. Which of these people will most likely be chosen for the extra safety check?

   A The 25th traveler in line

   B The 26th traveler in line

   C The 30th traveler in line

   D The 34th traveler in line

2. Shannon says, "My apartment number cannot be found using a factor of 3." Which could be Shannon's apartment number?

   A 15

   B 27

   C 31

   D 42

3. Jake said he ate $\frac{3}{4}$ of his dinner tonight. Which fraction is equivalent to $\frac{3}{4}$?

   A $\frac{2}{6}$

   B $\frac{4}{8}$

   C $\frac{9}{12}$

   D $\frac{10}{12}$

4. Kendra made 111 pastries for a bake sale. How many bags can she make if she puts 3 pastries in each bag? Are there any pastries left over?

   _____

5. Luis has $20. He buys 4 cans of tennis balls and gets $8 back as change. How much did one can of tennis balls cost?

   _____

6. What are the next two numbers in this pattern? Describe the pattern.

   $\frac{12}{12}$ $\frac{10}{12}$ $\frac{8}{12}$ $\frac{6}{12}$ ___ ___

   _____

   _____

   _____

   _____

   _____

1. Which fraction is equivalent to $\frac{1}{2}$?

   A $\frac{2}{6}$

   B $\frac{4}{8}$

   C $\frac{6}{10}$

   D $\frac{9}{12}$

2. Shaquille bought 3 jumbo packs of trading cards. Each jumbo pack contains 33 cards. How many trading cards did Shaquille buy?

   A 89 trading cards

   B 90 trading cards

   C 99 trading cards

   D 109 trading cards

3. What is the mixed number for $\frac{8}{3}$?

   A $1\frac{2}{3}$

   B $2\frac{2}{3}$

   C $3\frac{2}{3}$

   D $4\frac{2}{3}$

4. Which shows the fractions in order from greatest to least?

   A $\frac{1}{3}, \frac{1}{2}, \frac{1}{4}$

   B $\frac{1}{4}, \frac{1}{3}, \frac{1}{2}$

   C $\frac{1}{2}, \frac{1}{3}, \frac{1}{4}$

   D $\frac{1}{2}, \frac{1}{4}, \frac{1}{3}$

5. Write the unit fractions in order from least to greatest. Explain how you decided.

   $\frac{1}{4}, \frac{1}{12}, \frac{1}{2}, \frac{1}{10}, \frac{1}{6}, \frac{1}{3}$

   _____

   _____

   _____

   _____

   _____

   _____

6. **Mental Math** John took $\frac{4}{5}$ of the marbles from a jar. What fraction of the marbles were left in the jar?

   _____

7. There are 4 computer labs at a school. Each computer lab holds 15 computers. How many computers are there in all?

   _____

   _____

Name _____

1. There are 10 campers at Camp Davis. Three campers are swimming and 2 campers are hiking. Which fraction of the campers are swimming or hiking?

   A $\frac{1}{4}$

   B $\frac{1}{3}$

   C $\frac{1}{2}$

   D $\frac{2}{3}$

2. A pencil is $\frac{4}{10}$ of an inch wide. Which fraction is $\frac{4}{10}$ written in simplest form?

   A $\frac{2}{10}$

   B $\frac{2}{5}$

   C $\frac{3}{5}$

   D $\frac{8}{10}$

3. Which fraction is the sum of $\frac{2}{8} + \frac{4}{8}$ written in simplest form?

   A $\frac{1}{4}$

   B $\frac{3}{8}$

   C $\frac{1}{2}$

   D $\frac{3}{4}$

4. Which of the following is one way to decompose $1\frac{2}{3}$?

   A $\frac{2}{3} + \frac{1}{3} + \frac{1}{3}$

   B $\frac{2}{3} + \frac{2}{3} + \frac{1}{3}$

   C $\frac{1}{3} + \frac{1}{3} + \frac{1}{3}$

   D $\frac{1}{3} + \frac{2}{3} + \frac{3}{3}$

5. Find the missing value in the equation.

   $\frac{1}{6} + \frac{?}{6} = \frac{5}{6}$

   _____

6. Phoebe has 72 roses that she is putting into 5 vases. If she puts the same number of roses in each vase, how many roses are left over?

   _____

7. Tracy's soccer team plays 10 games in a season. Each game is 30 minutes long. Explain how you would find the number of hours Tracy's soccer team plays each season.

   _____

   _____

   _____

   _____

   _____

   _____

   _____

D 11·3

1. Karl has 10 shirts. Four shirts are green and 1 is blue. What fraction of Karl's shirts are green or blue?

   A $\frac{1}{4}$

   B $\frac{1}{3}$

   C $\frac{1}{2}$

   D $\frac{2}{3}$

2. Jack wrote this equation on the board, but Kim erased part of it.

   $$\frac{3}{12} + \frac{\square}{12} = \frac{7}{12}$$

   Which is the value of the missing numerator?

   A 4

   B 5

   C 10

   D 12

3. The outline of the shape of a unique city park is shown below. Each side is the same length. What is the length of a fence that encloses the entire park?

   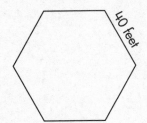

   40 feet

   A 160 feet

   B 200 feet

   C 240 feet

   D 280 feet

4. What is the sum of $\frac{2}{8} + \frac{1}{8} + \frac{3}{8}$ in simplest form?

   _____

5. Tyrone completed $\frac{3}{8}$ of a report on Wednesday. Then he completed $\frac{1}{2}$ of the report on Thursday. Did he complete more of his report on Wednesday or Thursday? Explain.

   _____

   _____

6. **Estimation** Josie read 246 pages of a book last month. Her older brother says he read about 3 to 4 times as many pages as Josie. Explain why 2,500 is **NOT** a reasonable estimate for the number of pages that Josie's brother read.

   _____

   _____

   _____

   _____

   _____

   _____

   _____

The map shows David's campsite, the park ranger's cabin, and Badger Lake at Hundred Pines State Park. Use the map to answer **1** and **2**.

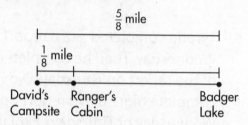

$\frac{5}{8}$ mile

$\frac{1}{8}$ mile

David's Campsite   Ranger's Cabin   Badger Lake

1. What is the distance from the ranger's cabin to Badger Lake expressed in simplest form?

  A $\frac{1}{8}$ mile

  B $\frac{1}{2}$ mile

  C $\frac{5}{8}$ mile

  D $\frac{3}{4}$ mile

2. David hikes from his campsite to the ranger's cabin and then back to his campsite. How far does David hike?

  A $\frac{1}{2}$ mile

  B $\frac{3}{8}$ mile

  C $\frac{1}{4}$ mile

  D $\frac{1}{8}$ mile

3. What is the sum of $\frac{2}{9} + \frac{4}{9}$ written in simplest form?

  A $\frac{1}{8}$

  B $\frac{1}{4}$

  C $\frac{1}{2}$

  D $\frac{2}{3}$

4. Find the sum.

$$\frac{1}{12} + \frac{4}{12}$$

_____

5. What is $\frac{10}{12}$ written in simplest form?

_____

6. In a survey, $\frac{4}{10}$ of students voted for less homework, while $\frac{2}{10}$ of students voted for fewer tests. What fraction of students voted either for less homework or fewer tests? Write your answer in simplest form.

_____

7. Ethan is 3 inches taller than Daisy. Let x = Ethan's height. Write an expression that represents Daisy's height. Explain how you decided which operation to use in your expression.

_____

_____

_____

_____

_____

Name _____

1. Shira has 20 books on her bookshelf. Of those, 15 are about horses. The rest are nature books. What fraction of Shira's books are about nature?

  A $\frac{1}{4}$

  B $\frac{1}{3}$

  C $\frac{2}{3}$

  D $\frac{3}{4}$

2. The table shows the amount of time four people spent exercising.

Exercise Log

Name	Time
Bill	$\frac{1}{2}$ hour
Carly	$\frac{3}{4}$ hour
Dimitri	$\frac{2}{3}$ hour
Emma	$\frac{2}{8}$ hour

Which person exercised for the least amount of time?

  A Bill   **C** Dimitri

  B Carly   **D** Emma

3. Which fraction is represented by point *M* on the number line below?

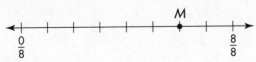

  A $\frac{1}{2}$ **C** $\frac{3}{4}$

  B $\frac{2}{3}$ **D** $\frac{4}{5}$

4. What is the difference of $\frac{5}{6} - \frac{1}{6} - \frac{2}{6}$ in simplest form?

_____

5. Rachel made 48 cookies. She wants to share them equally among 3 of her friends' families. How many cookies should she give to each family?

_____

6. Junior has 6 baseball cards and 4 basketball cards. What fraction of Junior's cards are basketball cards? Write your answer in simplest form.

_____

7. The numbers in this list follow a pattern. Write the missing number. Then describe the pattern you found.

  0   3   6   9 _____ 15   18   21

_____

_____

_____

Name _____

1. It takes 4 pounds of grapes to make 1 pound of raisins. How many pounds of grapes would you need to make 3,000 pounds of raisins?

   A 1,000 pounds

   B 6,000 pounds

   C 9,000 pounds

   D 12,000 pounds

2. Which number represents *n* in the diagram below?

   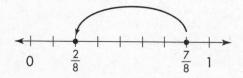

   A 7

   B 80

   C 700

   D 800

3. Which equation is modeled by this number line?

   A $\frac{7}{8} - \frac{5}{8} = \frac{2}{8}$

   B $\frac{7}{10} - \frac{5}{10} = \frac{2}{10}$

   C $\frac{2}{8} + \frac{5}{8} = \frac{7}{8}$

   D $\frac{2}{10} + \frac{5}{10} = \frac{7}{10}$

4. What is the sum of $\frac{9}{10}$ and $\frac{1}{10}$?

   _____

5. Jen needs to save $180 for a new camping tent. She is able to save $9 each week. How many weeks will Jen need to save to reach her goal? Draw a picture and write an equation to solve the problem. Explain how you found your answer.

   _____

   _____

   _____

   _____

   _____

   _____

   _____

   _____

Name _____

1. How would you write the number modeled below in standard form?

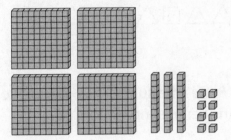

A 348

B 384

C 438

D 834

2. Which number completes the number sentence below?

$21 = \underline{\quad} + (6 + 8)$

A 6

B 7

C 14

D 35

3. Which fraction makes the number sentence true?

$\frac{3}{5} > \square$

A $\frac{4}{5}$

B $\frac{3}{6}$

C $\frac{4}{6}$

D $\frac{5}{6}$

4. The table below shows the populations of 4 cities.

City	Population
Happy Valley	49,604
Lakeside	50,104
Stoneyville	49,984
Rutherton	50,673

Write the populations in order from greatest to least.

_____

_____

5. Hilda has 9 trading cards. Kevin has 14 more cards than Hilda. Tom has 3 fewer cards than Kevin. Write a number sentence to show how many cards Tom has.

_____

6. Is the sum of $\frac{2}{7} + \frac{4}{7}$ closer to 0, $\frac{1}{2}$, or 1?

_____

7. Kelly ran $\frac{3}{8}$ of a race before stopping for water. Then she ran another $\frac{3}{8}$ of the race before stopping again. How much of the race does she have left to run? Write your answer in simplest form.

_____

Name _____

1. Rosalina's Flower Shop sells roses by the dozen. On Friday, Rosalina received an order for 21 dozen roses. How many roses does Rosalina need to fill the order?

   A 144 roses

   B 212 roses

   C 252 roses

   D 262 roses

2. What is 782,444 rounded to the nearest hundred thousand?

   A 900,000

   B 800,000

   C 700,000

   D 600,000

3. Which of the following numbers is **NOT** located correctly on the number line?

   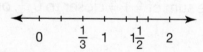

   A $\frac{1}{3}$

   B 1

   C $1\frac{1}{2}$

   D 2

4. Look at the pattern. Draw the next two figures.

    __ __

5. What is the sum $\frac{3}{12} + \frac{6}{12}$? Write your answer in simplest form.

   _____

6. In a game called four square, the court is made of a large square divided into 4 smaller squares. If 2 children are playing on 2 of the smaller squares, what part of the large square does not have any players?

   _____

7. **Mental Math** Joy makes toy boats out of balsa wood. Each boat uses three strips of wood. If Joy has 22 strips, how many boats can Joy make?

   _____

8. Write an equivalent fraction for $\frac{1}{5}$.

   _____

1. Tyrone was born in January of 1982. How old was Tyrone in February of 2013?

   A 24 years old

   B 31 years old

   C 54 years old

   D 74 years old

2. What is 456,982,000 written in expanded form?

   A 456,000 + 982,000

   B 400,000,000 + 50,000 + 6,000,000 + 900,000 + 80,000 + 2,000

   C 400,000,000 + 50,000,000 + 600,000 + 900,000 + 82,000

   D 400,000,000 + 50,000,000 + 6,000,000 + 900,000 + 80,000 + 2,000

3. Rosa made her favorite cookie recipe. Each batch makes 18 cookies. If Rosa made 5 batches, how many cookies did she make?

   A 23 cookies

   B 72 cookies

   C 90 cookies

   D 200 cookies

4. A number has a 4 in the thousands place and a 0 in the tens place. It has a 9 in the hundreds place and a 5 in the ones place. What is the number?

   _____

5. Mr. Tyler's class went to the planetarium. It costs $15 per student and $20 per adult. There were 20 students and 4 adults. How much did it cost altogether?

   _____

6. Christy made $240 in 5 days of work. Tasha made $280 in 7 days of work. Who made more money per day?

   _____

7. **Mental Math** Lauren had 26 baseball cards. She wanted to give each of her 4 brothers the same number of cards. How many cards did each of Lauren's brothers get? How many cards did Lauren have left over?

   _____

1. The table below shows a pattern. What is the missing number?

Input	Output
6	36
7	37
8	
9	39

A 38

B 48

C 83

D 88

2. The model is shaded to represent a number.

Which number is **NOT** represented by the model?

A $\frac{60}{100}$

B 0.6

C $\frac{6}{10}$

D 0.06

3. To meet regulations, a golf ball can only have 336 dimples. A small box contains 8 golf balls. There are a total of 2,800 dimples on all of the balls in the box. Do these golf balls meet regulations? Explain.

_____

_____

_____

4. Benjamin, Bradley, and Billy are brothers. Billy is 12 years old. Benjamin is 3 years younger than Billy. Bradley is 4 years older than Benjamin. List the brothers in age order, from youngest to oldest.

_____

_____

_____

5. **Estimation** Estimate the quotient: $735 \div 9$

_____

6. **Mental Math** Complete the fact family below.

_____ $\div 7 = 9$

_____ $\div 9 = 7$

$7 \times$ _____ = _____

$9 \times$ _____ = _____

Name _____

1. Which unit of measure would be best to measure the capacity of a large bucket?

   A Cups

   B Pints

   C Quarts

   D Gallons

2. **Mental Math** Steve has a piece of wood that is 8 feet long. He needs 2 feet to make a table leg. How many table legs can the piece of wood make?

   A 4 table legs   C 8 table legs

   B 6 table legs   D 10 table legs

3. Samuel weighs 10 lb more than Cheryl. Cheryl weighs 15 lb less than Eric. Eric's weight is 150 lb. How much does Samuel weigh?

   A 175 lb

   B 165 lb

   C 160 lb

   D 145 lb

4. What is the sum of $\frac{2}{8} + \frac{3}{8}$ in simplest form?

   A $\frac{5}{16}$

   B $\frac{5}{8}$

   C $\frac{6}{8}$

   D $\frac{3}{4}$

5. Marcia bought some carrots at the supermarket for $4. She gave the cashier a $20.00 bill. How much change did Marcia receive?

   _____

6. Ray drove 1,682 miles in 2 weeks. If he drove an equal number of miles each week, how many miles did Ray drive each week?

   _____

7. Sharon just bought a tank for her fish. How can she find the capacity of the tank? Explain.

   _____

   _____

   _____

   _____

   _____

   _____

   _____

1. Jamal is reading a book that is 52 pages long. Trisha is reading a book twice as long as Jamal's book. Amina is reading a book that has 3 times the number of pages as Trisha's book. How long is Amina's book?

   A 104 pages

   B 156 pages

   C 260 pages

   D 312 pages

2. Jorge has saved $53. His brother Marco has saved $11. If the brothers add their savings together, how much money will they have?

   A $42

   B $54

   C $64

   D $65

3. Mr. McBride is buying new clothes to wear to work. He purchased a shirt for $32, a pair of pants for $45, and a tie for $20. He pays with a hundred dollar bill. How much change will he get?

   A $80

   B $48

   C $23

   D $3

4. Look at the model below.

   What amount is shaded in the model? Write your answer in simplest form.

   _____

5. Write the number in standard form.

   $300,000 + 60,000 + 400 + 30 + 2$

   _____

6. Order the numbers from greatest to least.

   4.6, 1.3, 6.2

   _____

7. Gale, Stu, Cybil, Edwin, and Corey are standing in line at the movie theater. Corey is first in line. Stu is last in line. Gale is between Corey and Edwin. What is their order from front to back? Write the answer in a complete sentence.

   _____

   _____

   _____

1. Each shelf in the children's section of the library holds 76 books. If there are 18 shelves, how many books are in the children's section of the library?

   A 1,268 books

   B 1,368 books

   C 1,468 books

   D 1,568 books

2. A popular mid-size car weighs 3,412 pounds. A car trailer can haul 6 of these cars at one time. Which is the best estimate for the total weight of the 6 cars?

   A 12,000 pounds

   B 18,000 pounds

   C 24,000 pounds

   D 30,000 pounds

3. Ms. Santos wants to buy carpet for her living room. Which unit would she use to measure the width of the room?

   A Inch

   B Foot

   C Yard

   D Mile

4. Which is the shorter distance: 4 miles or 20,000 feet?

   _____

The table shows how many hours of homework three students did on Wednesday. Use the table for **5** and **6**.

Student	Time
Susan	$1\frac{1}{2}$ h
Dana	$2\frac{1}{6}$ h
Evelyn	$1\frac{3}{4}$ h

5. Which student spent the most time doing homework?

   _____

6. Which student spent the least time doing homework?

   _____

7. **Mental Math** Write a fact family for 8, 6, and 48.

   _____

   _____

   _____

Name _____

1. The model is shaded to represent a fraction.

Which model below shows an equivalent fraction?

A

B

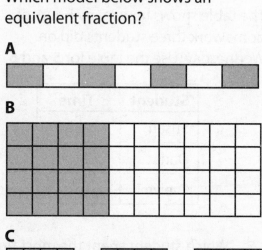

C

D

2. Jenny drew the face shown below.

The eyes are drawn with $\frac{2}{8}$ of the shapes Jenny used to draw the face. What is another way to describe the fraction of shapes used to draw the eyes?

A $\frac{1}{4}$ **C** $\frac{1}{6}$

B $\frac{4}{10}$ **D** $\frac{3}{9}$

3. Fred drew the pentagon below. The length of each side is 2 feet. How long is each side in inches?

_____

4. Mr. Nolan's class is holding a recycling drive. So far, the class has collected 183 aluminum cans. They want to collect a total of 1,000 cans. How many more cans do they need to collect?

_____

5. Eric has saved $8.05. His friend Emily has saved $6.55. How much money have the two friends saved in all?

_____

6. **Mental Math** Jeff has 5 cartons of eggs. Each carton has 12 eggs. How many eggs does Jeff have? Write and solve a number sentence that shows the problem.

_____

Name _____

1. The model is shaded to represent a fraction.

Which model below shows an equivalent fraction?

A

B

C

D

2. Amy looked at her watch when she got on the bus. She looked at it again when she arrived at school. How long was her bus trip?

Get on bus   Arrive at school

A 30 minutes

B 40 minutes

C 1 hour 5 minutes

D 1 hour 40 minutes

3. Franco drew the figure shown below. Each side is the same length. How long are the 6 sides altogether?

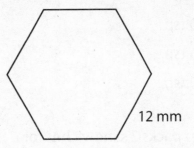

12 mm

4. A baseball field is designed so that the total distance around all the bases is 360 feet. If a player runs around the bases 5 times, how far has he run in feet?

_____

5. A parking lot has 4 sections. Each section can hold the same number of cars. If the lot can hold a total of 124 cars, how many can each section hold?

_____

6. Which customary unit of measure would you use to estimate the amount of water in an aquarium?

1. **Mental Math** How many teaspoons are in 5 tablespoons?

   A 5 tsp

   B 10 tsp

   C 15 tsp

   D 20 tsp

2. Phillip packs 2 sandwiches for lunch. Before school, he eats one half of a sandwich. How many sandwiches does he have left?

   A 3 sandwiches

   B $2\frac{1}{2}$ sandwiches

   C 2 sandwiches

   D $1\frac{1}{2}$ sandwiches

3. Tim has 13 rooms in his house. All but 2 rooms have 2 windows. The other 2 rooms have 1 window each. How many windows does he have in his house?

   A 26 windows

   B 24 windows

   C 13 windows

   D 2 windows

4. Pia ran $\frac{1}{5}$ of the race in first place and $\frac{3}{5}$ of the race in second place. What fraction of the race did Pia **NOT** run in first or second place?

   A $\frac{1}{5}$ **C** $\frac{4}{5}$

   B $\frac{3}{5}$ **D** 1

5. Which customary unit of measure would you use to estimate the amount of water in a coffee pot?

   _____

6. The length of the long side of the rectangle is 4 times longer than the short side. What is the length of the long side of the rectangle?

2 in.

   _____

7. Which is longer: a bed that is 7 feet long or a bed that is 77 inches long?

   _____

8. Jackie is twice as old as Karl. Karl is 3 years older than Kat. Kat is half as old as Gabe. Gabe is 10 years old. Write the names in order from oldest to youngest.

   _____

   _____

1. Four friends shared a pizza. The table below shows how much of the pizza each friend ate. Who ate the most pizza?

Pizza	
Name	**Amount of Pizza Eaten**
Felix	$\frac{1}{2}$
Lucy	$\frac{1}{8}$
Ned	$\frac{2}{8}$
Penny	$\frac{2}{16}$

A Felix

B Lucy

C Ned

D Penny

2. Olivia had 68 baseball cards. She gave 7 to Stephen. She then bought 12 more cards. How many cards does she have now?

A 49 cards

B 63 cards

C 73 cards

D 87 cards

3. Clinton spends 5 hours each month grocery shopping. How many hours does he spend grocery shopping in 1 year?

A 120 hours

B 60 hours

C 50 hours

D 12 hours

4. What are the length and width of the rectangle in centimeters?

20 mm

40 mm

5. Chessboards have 8 rows and 8 columns. How many squares are on a chessboard? Round your answer to the nearest ten.

6. Ken has 180 model cars. He stores his cars in 9 boxes. Each box has the same number of cars. How many cars are in each box?

7. Keagan went to the animal shelter with $200. She adopted a kitten for $85 and bought a carrier for $35 and a food dish for $8. How much money did she have left after the purchases? Explain.

Name _____

1. Brendan is adding to his CD collection. He buys 6 CDs at $15 each. How much money does he spend on the CDs?

   A $65

   B $70

   C $80

   D $90

2. Rosa says her baby sister is 1 yard tall. How tall is Rosa's sister in inches?

   A 48 inches

   B 40 inches

   C 36 inches

   D 20 inches

3. The table shows the numbers that were put into a machine and the different numbers that came out of the machine.

Input	Output
2	10
7	35
9	45
11	55

   Based on the information in the table, what happened to each number that was put into the machine?

   A It had 5 added to it.

   B It was multiplied by 5.

   C It had 5 subtracted from it.

   D It was divided by 5.

4. Evaluate the expression $g \times 11$ for $g = 5$.

   _____

5. Compare. Use $<$, $>$, or $=$.

   722,982 ◯ 722,892

6. Look for a pattern. Draw the next two shapes.

7. Write the word form of 363,239.

   _____

   _____

   _____

8. Add.

   $652 + 789 =$ _____

1. Molly is 10 times as old as her granddaughter, Anna. If Anna is 6 years old, how old is Molly?

   A 60 years old

   B 50 years old

   C 40 years old

   D 30 years old

2. The school librarian orders 35 new books each year. How many new books did the librarian order in the past 12 years?

   A 420 books

   B 354 books

   C 115 books

   D 47 books

3. Belinda's hair was 1 foot long. She cut off 8 inches. How many inches long is Belinda's hair now?

   A 3 inches

   B 4 inches

   C 5 inches

   D 9 inches

4. Jasper is 115 months old today. His friend Shawn had his 9th birthday exactly 2 months ago today. Is Jasper or Shawn older? Explain.

   _____

   _____

   _____

5. Write a number sentence to solve this problem. Karleen has 4 friends. She gives each friend 9 stickers. How many stickers does Karleen give away?

   _____

   _____

   _____

6. Selah has 5 CD cases. Each CD case holds 15 CDs. How many CDs can Selah store in the CD cases?

   _____

7. In order to read a 350-page book in 7 days, how many pages do you need to read each day if you read the same number of pages each day?

   _____

1. The table below shows the number of sit-ups that Cody did during the week.

Exercise Chart

Day	Number of Sit-Ups
Monday	29
Wednesday	37
Friday	81

How many sit-ups did Cody do for the whole week?

A 102 sit-ups

B 136 sit-ups

C 147 sit-ups

D 148 sit-ups

2. A grocery store has 40 boxes of granola bars on the shelves. There are 25 bars in each box. How many granola bars are there in all?

A 1,000 granola bars

B 800 granola bars

C 254 granola bars

D 100 granola bars

3. A newspaper reporter wrote an article about a recent football game. The attendance was 8,749, but the reporter rounded the number to the nearest hundred. Which number did the reporter use?

A 9,000   **C** 8,750

B 8,800   **D** 8,700

4. The length of a rectangle is twice as long as its width. If the width of the rectangle is 3 ft, what is the perimeter of the rectangle?

_____

_____

_____

_____

5. Sandy used $\frac{5}{6}$ of a carton of eggs in a recipe. Write an equivalent fraction for $\frac{5}{6}$.

_____

6. After school, Juan works packing boxes at the bookstore. Each box holds 5 books. How many boxes will he need to pack 120 books?

_____

7. Albert was asked to list four decimals between 0.25 and 0.50. What are four decimals he may have written?

_____

_____

_____

1. Ms. Franklin bought a used car for $7,250. She paid for the car in 5 equal payments. How much was each payment?

   A $105

   B $145

   C $1,050

   D $1,450

2. Each of 24 students in a class is given a set of building blocks. Each set has 16 blocks. How many blocks do the students have in all?

   A 144 blocks

   B 240 blocks

   C 344 blocks

   D 384 blocks

3. In 2010, there were 819,761 people living in South Dakota, and 900,877 people living in Delaware. How many more people lived in Delaware than in South Dakota?

   A 81,116 people

   B 91,116 people

   C 101,116 people

   D 119,116 people

4. Draw a rectangle that shows $\frac{7}{12}$. Explain how you made your drawing.

   _____

   _____

   _____

   _____

   _____

5. The smallest full-grown spider is about 0.4 mm in length. Write the decimal 0.4 as a fraction in simplest form.

   _____

6. **Mental Math** Elizabeth sold $\frac{3}{4}$ of 24 balloons at a festival. How many balloons did she sell?

   _____

Name _____

1. **Mental Math** Mr. Rudden saves $600 each month. How much money will he have saved after 6 months?

   A $1,200

   B $2,400

   C $3,600

   D $5,400

2. Monique wants to know the capacity of a bathtub. What unit of measure should she use?

   A cup

   B gallon

   C pint

   D quart

3. The population of Des Moines, Iowa, was 203,433 in 2010. What is the population rounded to the nearest ten thousand?

   A 200,000

   B 203,000

   C 203,400

   D 203,430

Shaquille drew the rectangle below.

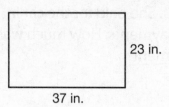

23 in.

37 in.

4. Find the perimeter of the rectangle Shaquille drew.

   _____

5. Find the area of the rectangle Shaquille drew.

   _____

6. What are the next two numbers in the pattern?

   7, 21, 63, 189, …

   _____

Name _____

1. Vanessa buys 4 tickets to a show. Each ticket costs $16. How much does she pay in all for the tickets?

   A $44

   B $54

   C $64

   D $74

2. A box of egg cartons holds 8 cartons of eggs. Each carton has a dozen eggs. How many eggs are in 5 boxes?

   A 40 eggs

   B 400 eggs

   C 480 eggs

   D 4,000 eggs

3. Which amount of money is the greatest?

   A 5 dimes, 2 nickels, 4 pennies

   B 2 quarters, 3 dimes

   C 1 quarter, 4 dimes, 4 nickels

   D 18 nickels

4. Anita has the money shown below. How much money does she have?

_____

5. **Mental Math** Write two fractions that are equivalent to $\frac{16}{24}$.

_____

_____

6. Luis wants to buy a new baseball glove. The glove he wants costs $85. He can save $5 each week. How many weeks will it take for him to save enough to buy the glove?

_____

Name _____

1. Four friends shared a pizza. The table below shows how much of the pizza each friend ate. Who ate the most pizza?

Pizza	
Name	**Amount of Pizza Eaten**
Felix	$\frac{1}{2}$
Lucy	$\frac{1}{8}$
Ned	$\frac{2}{8}$
Penny	$\frac{2}{16}$

  A Felix

  B Lucy

  C Ned

  D Penny

2. Olivia had 68 baseball cards. She gave 7 to Stephen. She then bought 12 more cards. How many cards does she have now?

  A 49 cards

  B 63 cards

  C 73 cards

  D 87 cards

3. Clinton spends 5 hours each month grocery shopping. How many hours does he spend grocery shopping in 1 year?

  A 120 hours   C 50 hours

  B 60 hours   D 12 hours

4. Beth drew the triangle shown below. What is the perimeter of the triangle?

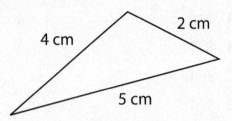

4 cm   2 cm   5 cm

_____

5. Chessboards have 8 rows and 8 columns. How many squares are on a chessboard? Round your answer to the nearest ten.

_____

_____

6. Ken walked for 7 hours to raise money for a charity. He raised $182. How much money did he raise for each hour he walked?

_____

Name _____

1. Which of the following are equivalent fractions?

  A $\frac{2}{6}$ and $\frac{4}{8}$

  B $\frac{1}{3}$ and $\frac{2}{4}$

  C $\frac{3}{4}$ and $\frac{6}{8}$

  D $\frac{4}{5}$ and $\frac{6}{10}$

2. Daniel wrote the following number sentence on his paper. What number makes the number sentence below true?

  $8 \times 7 > 4 \times \square$

  A 19

  B 18

  C 17

  D 12

3. Nick has $20. He wants to buy as many toy cars as he can. Each car costs $3. How many cars can he buy?

  A 6 cars

  B 7 cars

  C 17 cars

  D 23 cars

4. Harry has $\frac{3}{5}$ of his marble collection stored in a jar. Using marbles from the jar, Harry gives $\frac{1}{5}$ of his marbles to his friend. What fraction of his previous marble collection is left in the jar? Use the fraction strip to help you solve the problem.

_____

5. Gabrielle collected 68 trading cards. She shared them equally among 4 friends. How many cards did she give each of her friends?

_____

6. Jack started the pattern in the chart below. Continue the pattern to complete the chart.

10	19
20	29
30	39
40	

7. Jorge plans a 5-day road trip that totals 1,625 miles. He will drive the same number of miles each day. How many miles does he plan to drive each day?

_____

1. Four friends used a tape measure to find their heights in inches. Which shows their heights in order from least to greatest?

   A 39, 57, 46, 43

   B 43, 46, 57, 39

   C 39, 43, 46, 57

   D 57, 46, 43, 39

2. Jack has 106 toy cars. He gives 9 to his friend Steve and 41 to his sister Dana. How many toy cars does Jack have now?

   A 46 toy cars

   B 50 toy cars

   C 56 toy cars

   D 65 toy cars

3. Josh has 48 stickers and wants to share them with 8 friends. He wants to give each friend the same number of stickers. Which number sentence is in the same fact family as 48 ÷ 8 = ☐?

   A 48 × 6 = ☐

   B 6 × ☐ = 48

   C 48 ÷ 16 = ☐

   D ☐ × 8 = 16

4. **Estimation** Clint has 188 marbles. How many marbles does he have rounded to the nearest hundred?

   _____

5. If Jane rides her bike 15 miles each day for 12 weeks, how many miles will Jane have ridden her bike?

   _____

6. Hugo walked 2 miles on Thursday. He walked twice as many miles on Friday. On Saturday, he walked one mile more than he did on Friday. How many miles did Hugo walk on Saturday?

   _____

7. If the perimeter of the triangle below is 30 inches, what is the length of the third side?

   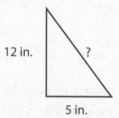

   12 in.   ?

   5 in.

   _____

Name _____

1. Tom has 12 compartments in his tackle box. In each compartment he has 5 fishing lures. How many fishing lures does he have in his tackle box?

   A 72 lures

   B 60 lures

   C 48 lures

   D 17 lures

2. Nick has $0.88 in his left pocket and $0.43 in his right pocket. How much money does he have in both pockets? Use the decimal grids shown below to help you add.

   A $0.31

   B $0.45

   C $1.21

   D $1.31

3. **Mental Math** Paula picked 180 blueberries. She plans to make 6 blueberry muffins and wants to have the same number of blueberries in each muffin. How many blueberries should she put into each muffin?

   A 120 blueberries

   B 90 blueberries

   C 60 blueberries

   D 30 blueberries

4. Jessica has two sticks. The sticks are the same distance apart at every point. How would you best describe the sticks?

   _____

   _____

5. Shade in the circle to show a fraction equivalent to $\frac{1}{2}$.

6. What is a geometric term for the lines below?

   _____

7. Hilary studied 25 minutes each day for five days this week. How long did Hilary study this week? Write your answer using hours and minutes.

   _____

1. Fran has 3 flowers growing in the window. They are $\frac{3}{4}$ foot, $\frac{2}{3}$ foot, and $\frac{5}{6}$ foot. Write the heights of the three flowers in order from least to greatest.

   A $\frac{2}{3}, \frac{3}{4}, \frac{5}{6}$

   B $\frac{2}{3}, \frac{5}{6}, \frac{3}{4}$

   C $\frac{5}{6}, \frac{2}{3}, \frac{3}{4}$

   D $\frac{5}{6}, \frac{3}{4}, \frac{2}{3}$

Use the figure shown for Exercises **2** and **3**.

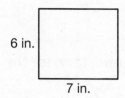

6 in.

7 in.

2. What is the area of the figure?

   A 13 square inches

   B 26 square inches

   C 42 square inches

   D 84 square inches

3. What is the perimeter of the figure?

   A 13 inches

   B 19 inches

   C 26 inches

   D 42 inches

4. A company buys 7 new photocopying machines. Each machine costs $4,619. What is the total cost of the machines?

   _____

5. **Estimation** Mr. Robbins has $2,730 in his checking account and $11,019 in his savings account. Round to the nearest hundred and add to find about how much money he has in both accounts combined.

   _____

6. What is the value of the underlined digit?

   9<u>8</u>6,592,013

   _____

7. Betty has 131 roses. She arranges 6 roses in each of 21 vases. How many roses does Betty have left over?

   _____

8. Liam worked 5 hours 30 minutes on Monday and 4 hours 45 minutes on Wednesday. How many total hours did Liam work on Monday and Wednesday?

   _____

1. Juana walks 2 miles every day. If she does this for 52 weeks, how many miles will she walk?

   A 54 miles

   B 104 miles

   C 364 miles

   D 728 miles

Use the figure shown for Exercises **2** and **3**.

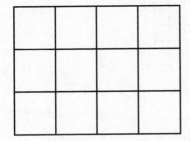

2. What fraction is equivalent to $\frac{8}{12}$?

   A $\frac{1}{2}$

   B $\frac{2}{3}$

   C $\frac{3}{4}$

   D $\frac{5}{6}$

3. What fraction is equivalent to $\frac{9}{12}$?

   A $\frac{2}{8}$

   B $\frac{4}{8}$

   C $\frac{3}{4}$

   D $\frac{5}{6}$

4. Gabrielle has 2,585 pennies. She wants to divide the pennies equally into 5 jars. How many pennies will go into each jar?

_____

5. **Estimation** A local minor league baseball team had 458,673 people show up to its games last summer. Round this number to the nearest hundred thousand.

_____

6. What type of angle is shown?

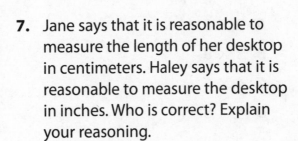

_____

7. Jane says that it is reasonable to measure the length of her desktop in centimeters. Haley says that it is reasonable to measure the desktop in inches. Who is correct? Explain your reasoning.

_____

_____

_____

_____

_____

_____

1. How much change would you get for a purchase of $7.67 if you paid with a $20 bill?

   A $10.62

   B $11.33

   C $12.33

   D $12.62

2. Zoe had 10 cookies and made 6 more. Then she gave 8 away. Which numerical expression can you use to find how many cookies Zoe has left?

   A $10 + (6 + 8)$

   B $(10 + 6) - 8$

   C $(12 - 10) + 8$

   D $12 + (10 - 8)$

3. **Mental Math** Which multiplication fact can help you find $32 \div 4$?

   A 2×8

   B 3×8

   C 4×6

   D 4×8

4. Folger Elementary School had 236 students. Then 7 more students came. Write a number sentence that shows the new number of students.

   _____

5. Write the word form for the decimal that is shaded below.

   _____

6. Write the missing numbers.

   1, 3, 5, 7, _____, _____, _____

7. Compare the numbers.

   102,732 ◯ 103,832

8. The maximum distance from Earth to Mars is 249,375,000 miles. What is this distance rounded to the nearest ten million?

   _____

Name _____

1. Kris is making a bowl of punch. He adds 5 quarts of cranberry juice, $1\frac{1}{2}$ gallons of orange juice, and 6 pints of pineapple juice. How much punch does Kris make?

   A 14 pints

   B 14 quarts

   C 17 quarts

   D 20 pints

2. Elizabeth ate 0.7 of an apple. What fraction is equivalent to 0.7?

   A $\frac{3}{5}$

   B $\frac{7}{10}$

   C $\frac{3}{4}$

   D $\frac{4}{6}$

3. Which number sentence is part of the same fact family as $7 \times 9 = 63$?

   A $63 \div 7 = \square$

   B $9 \times 63 = \square$

   C $7 + \square = 63$

   D $\square \div 63 = 9$

4. Rory has 3 rows of vegetables in his garden. Each row has 14 plants. How many plants does Rory have in his vegetable garden?

_____

5. **Mental Math** What number comes next in this pattern: 5, 11, 17, 23, 29, …?

_____

6. Danny drew the angle below. What is the measure of the angle Danny drew?

_____

7. Classify the angle that Danny drew in Exercise 6 as an acute angle, obtuse angle, or right angle.

_____

Name _____

1. Luke bought a keychain for $0.58. He gave the cashier $1.00. How much change should he get back?

   A $0.52

   B $0.42

   C $0.32

   D $0.12

2. Mrs. Pierce has 100 coins in her collection. She keeps the coins in 5 boxes. Each box has the same number of coins. How many coins are in each box?

   A 20 coins

   B 25 coins

   C 30 coins

   D 35 coins

3. Lynette drew the figure shown below. Each side of the figure has a length of 5 cm.

What is the perimeter of the figure?

   A 11 cm

   B 15 cm

   C 25 cm

   D 30 cm

4. **Estimation** A restaurant bought 13 boxes of ketchup. Each box has 32 bottles of ketchup. Write and solve a number sentence using compatible numbers to estimate the number of bottles the restaurant purchased.

_____

5. Which digit is in the hundred thousands place of 1,236,000?

_____

6. A spider has 8 legs. How many legs do 6 spiders have?

_____

7. Jacklynn draws two adjacent angles that form a right triangle. One angle measures 32°. What is the measure of the other angle?

_____

8. A rectangular pool has a length of 16 feet and a width of 32 feet. What is the area of the pool?

_____

Name _____

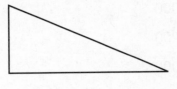

1. **Estimation** Mrs. Jackson has 806 songs on her computer. How many songs does she have rounded to the nearest ten?

   A 800 songs

   B 805 songs

   C 810 songs

   D 900 songs

2. Harvey can read 17 pages in one hour. In one month, he spent 12 hours reading. How many pages did Harvey read that month?

   A 204 pages

   B 194 pages

   C 104 pages

   D 51 pages

3. John has $0.72. His sister has $0.21. How much do they have together?

   A $0.63

   B $0.73

   C $0.83

   D $0.93

4. Classify the triangle below by its sides and by its angles.

   _____

5. Wendell has 213 craft sticks. He uses 114 craft sticks to make a model house. How many does he have left over?

   _____

6. An equilateral triangle has a perimeter of 45 ft. What is the length of each side of the triangle?

   _____

7. José says that 100 is a perfect square. How can José justify his statement?

   _____

   _____

   _____

1. **Estimation** What is 530,938 rounded to the nearest thousand?

   A 530,000

   B 530,900

   C 531,000

   D 500,000

2. Gavin is 48 inches tall. How many feet is this?

   A 4 feet   C 16 feet

   B 12 feet   D 144 feet

3. Seth has a stamp collection. His mother is going to give him 4 stamps. What can Seth do to find out how many stamps he will have after getting stamps from his mother?

   A Add 4 to the number of stamps he has now.

   B Multiply the number of stamps he has now by 4.

   C Divide the number of stamps he has now by 4.

   D Subtract 4 from the number of stamps he has now.

4. Jan has five $1 bills, 3 quarters, and 4 dimes. How much money does she have?

   A $6.45   C $6.25

   B $6.35   D $6.15

5. Jonathan draws the figure below. He says that he drew a quadrilateral. Is Jonathan correct? Explain.

   _____

   _____

   _____

   _____

6. A camper has 6 storage compartments. Each compartment can hold 3 sleeping bags. If there are 17 sleeping bags to be stored, how many compartments will be used? How many sleeping bags will be in the compartment that is not completely filled?

   _____

   _____

   _____

   _____

7. Juan bought a sweater for $15.95 and two shirts for $9.00 each. How much did Juan spend on clothes?

   _____

Name _____

1. The table below shows how much money four family members spent on their vacation.

Name	Amount Spent
Brenda	$16.70
Kirk	$17.76
Allison	$61.70
Lee	$17.60

Which of the following shows the money amounts in order from greatest to least?

A $17.60, $16.70, $61.70, $17.76

B $61.70, $17.76, $16.70, $17.60

C $16.70, $17.60, $17.76, $61.70

D $61.70, $17.76, $17.60, $16.70

2. Mental Math Tyler drew a line that was 5 feet long. How many inches are in five feet?

A 12 inches

B 36 inches

C 48 inches

D 60 inches

3. Where would placing the number 7 make the number sentence true?

A $9 \times \square = 72$

B $\square \times 8 = 56$

C $4 \times \square = 48$

D $\square \times 7 = 77$

4. What is $\frac{4}{12}$ in simplest form?

_____

5. Taryn cuts an equilateral triangle and a square out of wood. The figures have the same perimeter. What are possible side lengths of the triangle and square?

_____

_____

_____

_____

_____

6. The Kings County school district has 487 fourth-grade students. Of these, 251 are girls. How many boys are in the fourth grade?

_____

7. How many lines of symmetry does the figure below have? Draw each one.

Name _____

1. Ben works at a pet store. He has $452 to buy new cat toys for the store. Each toy costs $4. How many toys can Ben buy?

    A 448 toys

    B 226 toys

    C 113 toys

    D 87 toys

2. Which number is the greatest?

    A 4.01

    B 4.0

    C 3.99

    D 2.7

3. Mr. Conner is 6 feet tall. How tall is he in inches?

    A 84 inches

    B 72 inches

    C 68 inches

    D 60 inches

4. Two adjacent angles form a 135° angle. If one of the angles measures 48°, what is the measure of the other angle?

    A 42°

    B 87°

    C 132°

    D 183°

5. What is the measure of the angle?

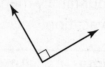

_____

6. Order the fractions from least to greatest: $\frac{11}{12}, \frac{1}{2}, \frac{5}{8}, \frac{1}{4}$.

_____

7. In the number 32.14, which digit is in the hundredths place?

_____

8. Sophia buys two bags of carrots at $3.49 each, three big bottles of juice for $0.89 each, and 4 bags of celery for $1.29 each. Estimate how much she spent by rounding each item to the nearest dollar. Explain how you estimated.

_____

_____

_____

_____

_____

1. Which fraction is the same as 0.23?

A $\frac{23}{10}$

B $\frac{1}{4}$

C $\frac{23}{100}$

D $\frac{1}{23}$

2. Roger drives steadily and travels 440 miles in eight hours. How many miles does he travel in one hour?

A 50 miles

B 55 miles

C 60 miles

D 65 miles

3. At the pet store where Hannah works, there are 9 fish tanks. Each tank has 72 fish in it. How many fish are there in total?

A 648 fish

B 638 fish

C 9 fish

D 8 fish

4. The scores on the most recent history test were 88, 81, 90, 55, 79, 95, 82, 91, 100, 80, 86, 93, 87, 98, 94. Which score is an outlier?

A 100

B 79

C 55

D There are no outliers.

5. Karl recorded how many days each month he played outside. He then plotted the data on a bar graph.

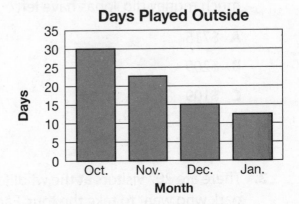

Days Played Outside

How many more days did Karl play outside in October than in December?

_____

6. Kary is 5 feet tall. Laurie is 63 inches tall. Who is taller? Explain.

_____

_____

_____

7. Write three decimals that are greater than 0.4 but less than 0.5.

_____

_____

Name _____

1. Jonas made $407 by doing chores around the neighborhood. He spent $298 on a new DVD player. How much money did Jonas have left?

    A $715

    B $209

    C $109

    D $15

2. There are 207 visitors at the wildlife park who want to take the tour. Each tour van has 9 seats. How many vans are needed to take all the visitors on the tour?

    A 10 vans   C 20 vans

    B 13 vans   D 23 vans

3. There are 18 flower seeds in each packet. Mr. Doyle buys 4 packets. How many flower seeds does he buy?

    A 432 seeds   C 56 seeds

    B 72 seeds   D 42 seeds

4. Selena is decorating square tiles to use in her kitchen. One side of each tile is 12 centimeters. What is the perimeter of each tile?

    A 12 cm

    B 24 cm

    C 48 cm

    D 84 cm

5. Brian said that 4,449 rounded to the nearest hundred was 4,500 because 4,449 rounded to the nearest ten is 4,450 and 4,450 rounds to 4,500. Is he correct? Explain.

    _____

    _____

    _____

    _____

    _____

6. Look for a pattern. What are the next two numbers in this pattern?

    1, 3, 7, 13, 21, 31, 43, 57, _____ , _____

7. Write $\frac{9}{12}$ in simplest form.

    _____

8. What is the area of the rectangle below?

    17 in.

    6 in.

    _____

Name _____

1. Yvette's computer has a folder with files shown in rows and columns. There are 4 rows and 12 columns. Which number sentence will tell you how many files the folder has?

   A $4 \times 12 = 48$

   B $12 - 4 = 8$

   C $4 + 12 = 16$

   D $12 \div 4 = 3$

2. Last year a bagel shop sold eighty-four thousand, seven hundred six bagels. What is this number in standard form?

   A 840,760   **C** 84,760

   B 840,706   **D** 84,706

3. Nick has 1,263 baseball cards. He gives 374 to his younger sister. How many baseball cards does Nick have now?

   A 889 baseball cards

   B 899 baseball cards

   C 989 baseball cards

   D 999 baseball cards

4. Which of the following numbers is less than 468,112?

   A 470,000   **C** 468,125

   B 469,000   **D** 468,100

5. What kind of lines are shown?

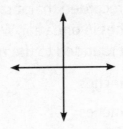

   _____

6. Lorinda has basketball practice each afternoon at 4:00 P.M. Practice is 90 minutes long. What time is basketball practice over?

   _____

7. Henry bought a gallon of milk on Monday. That day, he drank 2 cups of milk. On Tuesday, he drank 1 cup of milk and his brother had 2 cups of milk. On Wednesday, both Henry and his brother drank 1 cup of milk. How many cups of milk are left in the gallon?

   _____

8. The key to a stem-and-leaf plot reads: Key: 11 | 5 = 11.5

   What does 9 | 8 mean in the same stem-and-leaf plot?

   _____

1. **Estimation** The rain gauge at the airport recorded that it rained 127 inches in one year. What is this amount rounded to the nearest ten?

   A 100 inches

   B 110 inches

   C 120 inches

   D 130 inches

2. Kate writes two equivalent fractions for the shaded part of the rectangle.

   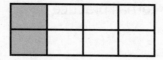

   What two fractions could Kate write?

   A $\frac{2}{6}$ and $\frac{4}{12}$

   B $\frac{2}{8}$ and $\frac{1}{4}$

   C $\frac{2}{8}$ and $\frac{4}{8}$

   D $\frac{6}{8}$ and $\frac{2}{8}$

3. Josh spends 9 hours each week doing homework. The school year is 36 weeks long. How many hours of homework does Josh do in one school year?

   A 468 hours

   B 368 hours

   C 324 hours

   D 274 hours

4. Draw an obtuse angle.

5. Nana scored 4,591 points on Space Ranger. Her friend Natriz scored 692 more points. How many points did Natriz score?

   _____

6. Order the students from shortest to tallest.

Student	Height (in meters)
Josh	1.5
Sarah	1.31
Danielle	1.29
Michael	1.3

   _____

   _____

7. Wendy bought six books for $3 each. How much change did she receive if she paid with a $20 bill?

   _____

1. Which digit is in the hundreds place of the number 34,863?

   A 8

   B 6

   C 4

   D 3

2. **Mental Math** Which is equal to 2 quarters and 9 dimes?

   A 4 quarters and 3 dimes

   B 14 dimes

   C 4 quarters and 5 dimes

   D 15 dimes

3. Penelope had $8.56. She bought a carton of milk for $0.35. How much money does she have left?

   A $8.51

   B $8.21

   C $7.21

   D $5.06

4. Which fraction is equivalent to $\frac{4}{12}$?

   A $\frac{3}{4}$

   B $\frac{1}{2}$

   C $\frac{1}{3}$

   D $\frac{1}{4}$

5. Mr. Nolan's class sponsors a recycling drive. So far, the class has collected 183 aluminum cans. They want to collect a total of 1,000 cans. How many more cans do they need to collect?

   _____

6. Write the decimal modeled below.

   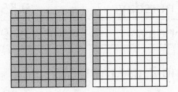

   _____

7. Mindy is 7 years old. Her sister Mary is 14 years old. When Mary is 24, how old will Mindy be?

   _____

8. What number comes next in the pattern below?

   1, 2, 4, 7, 11, 16, 22, . . .

   _____

Students at Wood Elementary School participated in a "Penny Challenge." Ms. Brenner's class used the chart below to keep track of the amount of money they raised each day.

Day	Amount of Money
Monday	$ 4.74
Tuesday	6.23
Wednesday	11.78
Thursday	9.55
Friday	12.49

In **1** and **2**, use the table.

1. What is the total amount of money Ms. Brenner's class raised?

   A $42.79

   B $44.79

   C $44.99

   D $45.09

2. What is the difference between the amount Ms. Brenner's class raised on Friday and the amount they raised on Monday?

   A $7.75

   B $8.75

   C $16.23

   D $17.23

3. Baseball bats cost $23.50. Mitts cost $35.00. How much will it cost to buy 2 mitts and 1 baseball bat?

   _____

   _____

4. Three boys plan to contribute an equal amount of money in order to buy a present. The present costs $135. How much will each boy contribute?

   _____

5. Betty has 131 roses. She puts 6 roses in each of 21 vases. How many roses does Betty have left over?

   _____

6. Order the fractions from least to greatest:

   $$\frac{8}{16} \quad \frac{3}{12} \quad \frac{3}{4} \quad \frac{1}{6}$$

   _____

Name _____

1. Mr. Mason deposits $110 into his savings account every 2 weeks. So far, he has saved $1,980. How much money will he have saved after his next deposit?

A $110

B $1,090

C $1,870

D $2,090

2. The model is shaded to represent a fraction.

Which model below shows an equivalent fraction?

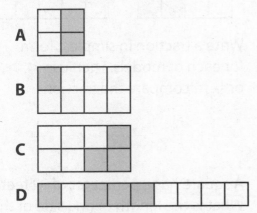

3. A hospital was the site of 76,534 births in one year. A newspaper writer rounded the number to the nearest thousand. Which number did the writer use?

A 80,000 **C** 77,000

B 77,500 **D** 70,000

4. How many hours are in 3 days?

_____

5. Write the decimals shown below in order from least to greatest.

6.2   5.32   6.07   5.19

_____

Write a number sentence to solve the problem below.

6. At the beginning of the month, Cheree had $529.16 in her checking account. During that month, she deposited a total of $297.18 and withdrew a total of $159.10. How much money did Cheree have in her account at the end of the month?

_____

_____

7. At a camp there are 39 cabins. Each cabin has 6 windows. How many windows are there in all?

_____

Name _____

1. A bowling alley has 10 pins in each lane. There are 24 lanes. How many pins are in the bowling alley?

   A 24 pins

   B 240 pins

   C 2,400 pins

   D 24,000 pins

2. William has 143 books. What is 143 rounded to the nearest ten?

   A 200

   B 140

   C 110

   D 100

3. Which shows the numbers in order from greatest to least?

   A 1.81, 1.8, 1.18, 1.08

   B 1.08, 1.18, 1.8, 1.81

   C 1.8, 1.81, 1.18, 1.08

   D 1.8, 1.81, 1.08, 1.18

4. Which fraction is equivalent to $\frac{6}{16}$?

   A $\frac{1}{6}$

   B $\frac{3}{8}$

   C $\frac{6}{10}$

   D $\frac{10}{16}$

5. Tracey has 187 stamps in her collection. Her grandmother gives her 42 more stamps. How many stamps does Tracey have in all?

_____

6. Grant has 333 toothpicks. He gets 3 more. How many toothpicks does he have in all rounded to the nearest hundred?

_____

7. The shaded areas are the reserved rooms at a conference center.

West Hall Rooms 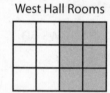   East Hall Rooms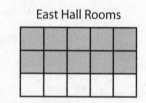

Write a fraction in simplest form for each of models. Then use <, >, or = to compare the fractions.

_____

8. A square has a perimeter of 92 feet. What is the length of one side of the square?

_____

1. Mr. Plant owns a bicycle store. He sells 6 different kinds of bikes and has 222 bikes in the store. He has an equal number of each kind of bike. How many of each kind of bike does he have?

   A 37 bikes

   B 42 bikes

   C 47 bikes

   D 52 bikes

2. Jim has 4 plants. He measured the height of each plant in centimeters. Which of the following shows the heights of the plants in order from tallest to shortest?

   A 21 cm, 42 cm, 33 cm, 36 cm

   B 21 cm, 33 cm, 42 cm, 36 cm

   C 36 cm, 42 cm, 33 cm, 21 cm

   D 42 cm, 36 cm, 33 cm, 21 cm

3. Ms. Jones calculated the average scores for each of her fourth-grade math classes on a recent test. Which of the following is a true statement about the averages?

   A 92.1 < 92.05

   B 92.05 < 93.01

   C 93.01 < 92.10

   D 92.10 < 92.1

4. Tell whether each angle is acute, obtuse, or right.

   _____

   _____

   _____

5. In the number 34,278,915, give the place values of the following digits.

   7: _____

   9: _____

   5: _____

6. Use a basic multiplication fact to find the product below.

   $90 \times 70 =$

   _____

7. Which is longer, 6 yards or 220 inches?

   _____

Name _____

1. A manatee can eat about 100 pounds of food per day. How much food can a manatee eat in one week?

   A 70 pounds

   B 700 pounds

   C 7,000 pounds

   D 70,000 pounds

2. The table below shows how many hours each class spent working in the school garden. How many hours did all the classes work in the garden?

Work in School Garden	
Class	**Hours in Garden**
Mrs. Eismen	99
Ms. Taylor	72
Mr. Santi	138

   A 210 hours   **C** 237 hours

   B 309 hours   **D** 471 hours

3. Alex earns a $15 allowance each week. This week she spent $4.18 on a gift for her father and $8.84 on ice-skating. If she saves the rest of her allowance, how much money does she save?

   A $1.68

   B $1.78

   C $1.88

   D $1.98

4. Which streets are parallel to each other on the map below?

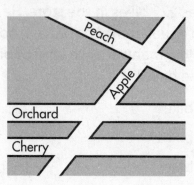

5. In science class, Ben was given 0.6 gram of salt for an experiment. Karen was given 0.09 gram of salt. Tony was given 0.57 gram of salt. Terry was given 0.8 gram of salt. Order the measures of salt from least to greatest.

6. At Davidson's Restaurant Supplies Warehouse, plastic forks come in boxes of 750. Lucy's Diner ordered 5 boxes of plastic forks. How many plastic forks did Lucy's Diner order?